CHANGING MAN:
THE THREAT AND THE PROMISE

CHANGING MAN:
THE THREAT AND THE PROMISE

*Five Scientists and Five Theologians on
Christian Faith and Evolutionary Thought*

EDITED BY

KYLE HASELDEN AND PHILIP HEFNER

Anchor Books
Doubleday & Company, Inc.
Garden City, New York

Changing Man: The Threat and the Promise was originally published in a hardbound edition by Doubleday & Company, Inc. in 1968.

Anchor Books edition: 1969

PREFACE

A few years ago a long-time friend of *The Christian Century*—Miss Anna Grace Sawyer, now of Evanston, Illinois—suggested to the editors of this journal that it should publish a series of articles exploring the current relation of Christian faith and evolutionary thought. This perceptive and helpful suggestion was based primarily on Miss Sawyer's awareness that many Christians still ignore or stubbornly disregard the challenge that nineteenth-century evolutionary theory put to biblical literalism and to static Christian views of the nature of man. This continuing condition was in itself a sufficient warranty for the publication of such a series, but the proposal appealed to the editors of the *Century* even more because of their awareness that another group of Christians has too lightly assumed that all of the controversies between the faith and the science were permanently resolved in the past and at the expense of the faith. The editors therefore accepted Miss Sawyer's proposal with the hope that they might devise a set of articles that would help correct both of these mistakes in Christian reaction to evolutionary thought.

If the series published by *The Christian Century* in 1967 met this objective, credit goes to the editors' success in securing able professional assistance for their venture into a field in which they did not consider themselves expert. They were especially fortunate in procuring the help of Dr. Philip Hefner in outlining the series and in securing contributions to it from the ablest scholars in this field. It was a joy to work with him in the original publication of the series and in presenting it in book form.

The editors of this book express gratitude to The Christian Century Foundation for permission to republish these articles and to Doubleday & Company, Inc. for its patient co-operation in making this book possible. We also thank the contributors, all of whom fulfilled their assignments at high levels of scholarship and most of whom met rigorous deadline schedules faithfully. Portions of Dr. William T. Keeton's article are based on passages in his book *Biological Science* and are used by permission of the publisher, W. W. Norton and Company. With the exception of the preface, the introduction, the bibliography and the index—none of which were published in *The Christian Century*—all articles were edited by members of *The Christian Century* staff: Dean Peerman, Margaret Frakes and Cecelia Gaul. We are indebted to them for the skill with which they styled and perfected manuscripts for publication. I must also express our gratitude to my secretary, Elaine Kreis, for her indispensable help in typing manuscripts and in handling the numerous details involved in such an enterprise.

Kyle Haselden

CONTENTS

INTRODUCTION

PHILIP HEFNER

Within the covers of this volume there is contained the beginning of a conversation between five scientists and five theologians on evolutionary theory and Christian faith. If the reader accepts this conversation for what it is, namely a conversation and not a seminar or a lecture series or the working-out of one man's synthesis between science and theology, then it may serve him as a handy primer, a foot in the door to the particular kinds of issues and problems that figure in the conversation between evolutionary theory and Christian faith in the mid-1960s.

The very fact of the conversation is a mark that we are in the mid-twentieth century, rather than the turn of the century. The acrimony of that earlier time has largely died out, so that the conversation here is not at all unusual, but typical of a growing concern for the interrelationship between things religious and things scientific. Our memories of the battles between Darrow and Bryan at the Scopes trial in Tennessee, or between the elder Huxley and Bishop Wilberforce in England remind us how fruitless and wasteful that earlier exchange was.

As concerned as we were to leave behind us that exchange, we must not let the images of those debates, together with the rise of Fundamentalism in the first two decades of this century, stereotype our image of the response that previous generations of Christians made to evolutionary theory. The conversation in this book has not sprung full-blown from Zeus's head; it has its roots in a strong tradition of American thought, and a comparison with that tradition will illumine the peculiarities of our present conversation. It is true that there was a widespread repudiation of evolutionary theory among the American churches during the first fifty years after Darwin did his work. But it is also true, as Stowe Persons remarks, that Protestantism in nineteenth century America was not simply inflexible or reactionary in the face of modernity; that Protestantism was able to, and in fact did, make creative responses to the Darwinian evolutionary thinking that swept our society in the second half of the last century. Men like John Fiske, James McCosh, and Asa Gray were quick and energetic to respond constructively to the new Darwinism.

The first wave of American theological response to evolutionary thought was chiefly philosophical and apologetic. American theologians were concerned to augment their vision of God's ways with man and his plan for the creation by means of the evolutionary scheme of thought. These theologians had to be apologists, because evolutionary theory threatened some classical Christian positions. It seriously challenged the primacy of the biblical stories of creation, as well as the classical ways of understanding God's manner of creation and man's dignity as a unique creation whose origins and destiny are sharply differentiated from the rest of nature. As apologists, they had to demonstrate that despite these onslaughts, evolutionary schemes deepened the biblical-Christian faith. But these earlier theologians had also to be philosophers, because they were intent upon demonstrating that evolution opened up new vistas in the knowledge of God; indeed, evolution became quasi-revelatory in character for these theologians.

Students of American history have noted how the theory of natural selection was utilized to elaborate the Calvinist concern for God's providence, concluding that the mechanisms of the survival of the fittest operated because God wanted them to operate. Another group of theologians, perhaps predisposed by a Romantic idealism, allied themselves with a Spencerian doctrine of culture, concluding that evolution and progress were united in a march toward salvation, love, the growth of intelligence, peace, and virtue—all under the direction of God's plan.

Whatever generalizations one might draw about the initial philosophical and apologetic theological response to evolutionary thought may be crystallized in a closer look at one typical theologian of the period, Newman Smyth. Smyth (1843–1925), scion of an illustrious New England Congregational family, taught at Bowdoin and Andover Theological School, before he was forced into exile by more reactionary ecclesiastical powers. He was elected a Fellow of Yale University, where he spent the last twenty-five years of his life reflecting and writing upon evolution and Christian faith. His three most important books upon this theme were *The Place of Death in Evolution* (1897), *Through Science to Faith* (1904), and *Constructive Natural Theology* (1913).

Smyth was not afraid of the eroding effects of evolutionary theory. He believed, on the contrary, that evolution in nature is revelatory of God's operations and his will, so that any insights derived from evolutionary processes must necessarily be complementary to revelation acquired from the Bible. This theologian was in search of the truth, God's truth, and he was willing to immerse himself in the biological theories, in order to utilize that particular avenue to the truth. He looked upon this work as an exercise in natural theology, by which the empirical work of the "single-eyed observer" might be interpreted so as to be fertilized by philosophical and theological analysis. This fertilization would render evolutionary data fruitful for a larger understanding of life. Smyth's description of his method includes a close study of the facts which biologists have observed, in which he would "accept and make the most of their theories or explanations of the observed facts, so far as they may be made to go"; but he intended also to "inquire what may be their higher and larger significance for our rational and religious conception of the world . . . (that we may work) toward a more scientifically spiritual understanding of the creation."

Smyth rested his natural evolutionary theology on two foundational ideas, namely, that evolution revealed that there was an Intelligence which guided the development of nature and that this development was in a continuum from the simplest matter to Spirit, which culminated in Christ. These two ideas fulfilled both the apologetic and the philosophical tasks. They persuaded Smyth that evolution led one eventually to the God who undergirded Christian faith, and therefore one could effectively urge Christianity upon the modern man who accepted evolution. At the same time, for one who was looking for God, evolution could be recommended because of the philosophical insights it afforded into the nature of the created order and God's plan within that order. Creation, death, evil were all transmuted from their literal accounts in the Bible into patterns that were commensurate with evolutionary theory: death was utilitarian, for the progress of life; evil was a developmental challenge to be overcome; creation was the process itself.

It would be impossible for the conversation recorded in this volume to follow the lines of Newman Smyth's thought. On the one hand, he permitted his enthusiasm for the new science of biology to dilute, or at least disregard, the biblical picture of faith in a manner that no post-Barthian theologian (or scientist, for that matter) could tolerate. Although Smyth himself conceived his natural theology as a prelude to revealed theology, he identified God and evolution, overlooked the depth and tragedy of evil, in ways that are no longer possible for Christian theologians. The theologians represented in this volume stand worlds apart from Smyth in this respect. On the other hand, Smyth extrapolated so easily from the data of biology to the philosophy of nature and life, that he falls under philosophical criticism. Professor Holmer's essay reflects perhaps most sharply the current reticence to build a philosophy upon biology. Even the more metaphysical essays of Messrs. Dobzhansky, Barbour, and Hefner are quite unwilling to leap so facilely from biology to ontology as Smyth does. Nevertheless, given their greater sensitivity to the tradition of biblical faith and to the philosophical problems that attend the movement from biology to the larger world-view, the essays in this volume share Smyth's concern that one need not relinquish his faith in order to accept evolutionary thinking; the insights which are available to the biologist are not irrelevant to the knowledge of God.

It would be naive for the present conversationalists on evolution not to acknowledge the tradition of concern for evolution that has marked liberal American theological thinking in the past. But it would be just as naive and distorting if we failed to recognize the decidedly new factors which have entered the conversation within the past fifty years, and which definitely mark this volume. In the half century since Smyth and his colleagues did their work, we have grown not only in our reluctance to extrapolate from scientific hypotheses to metaphysics, but also much more sophisticated about what science in general and biology in particular can accomplish in our world. The almost unlimited vistas of scientific achievement which we hold today make Smyth's era seem antiquated. Moreover, we are now conscious in a way that his generation was not that this scientific achievement, coupled with man's total cultural life, can be and is giving man unprecedented control over his own development, that cultural evolution is superseding (not abolishing) biological evolution. This sophistication about man's power to shape his own development gives us a much larger view of what man can accomplish, but also a much deeper realism into the fallibilities of man's efforts, and a much more haunting fear that man may guide his own development into a cul-de-sac from which there is no escape. Since so much of man's power to shape his own future is concentrated in the biological sciences which concern themselves most closely with evolutionary theory, it is not surprising that in discussing evolution, the writers in this series could never forget completely the problems that attend man's control of his evolution.

In other words, the *ethical* consideration that accompanies the technological development of the biological sciences has cropped up in this current conversation on evolutionary theory in a way that is almost totally foreign to the discussions of evolution in an earlier epoch of American history. This concern—even anxiety—over the control of man's evolutionary development is poignantly distinctive of this particular time in American history and world history, the time when the technological present is very certain, almost overpowering, while the future which that technology of biology and medicine will bring is so uncertain, its outlines so foreboding through the mist of that uncertainty.

It is not difficult to discern why the ethical dimension of biology and evolutionary theory should loom so large in the present conversation. But at the same time, it is not difficult to see also that no matter how urgent the ethical issues are, and no matter how high their priority over other dimensions of this conversation, there are other dimensions that cannot be overlooked if the conversation is to retain its equilibrium. Most importantly, there are philosophical-theological dimensions, which form a link to the discussions of previous generations and a backdrop against which the ethical issues can be understood and elaborated more clearly. These philosophical issues crop up in four of the essays—this introduction, and the pieces by Gilkey, Holmer, and Barbour. If the reader attends to the ethical concern that is represented in most of the essays, he will have an accurate sense of what animates the spirits of theologians and scientists as they explore the implications of modern biology and evolutionary theory. On the other hand, if the reader attends to the more philosophical and theological concerns that appear in a few of the other essays, he will glimpse the intellectual structure in which the ethical problems have arisen, just as he will begin to understand that our present resolution of the ethical problems requires of us a thorough rethinking of our presuppositions about man and his purpose in this world.

Our present task, then, is to summarize some of the broader philosophical-theological issues raised by these essays, under five headings: (1) the biological significance of the moral and spiritual phenomena, (2) the relationship of spirit and matter, (3) freedom and determinism, (4) the relationship of God to nature, (5) change as constitutive of reality.

The Biological Significance of Moral and Spiritual Phenomena

Because evolutionary theory emphasizes the bond which ties all levels of being together, from relatively simple chemical substances to man himself, evolutionary thinkers have from the beginning interpreted the so-called "higher" realities of morality and spirit in relationship to the biological realm. One tendency has been to insist that there is some primal energy or force (called "life") which irresistibly developed, unfolding itself in its transcendence of matter, up through the spectrum of living things until it reached its zenith in man and his spirit. This tendency, since called "vitalism," was able to value biological development as the necessary path by which the vital force came to expression, eventually reaching its highest form in spirit. This position has nearly disappeared among biologists today, simply because the development of living forms can be explained by the mechanisms of natural selection with no need to postulate so mysterious a category as "vital force."

Another tendency has reduced the life of morality and spirit to a function of the mechanisms of natural selection. According to this point of view, phenomena like morality and religion are simply ways of adapting to the environment, ways which may be manipulated accordingly, ways which may indeed be undesirable and now superseded. This tendency shares all of the fallacies of any reductionism, and its cogency is diminished accordingly. Theologians, moreover, have insisted that their spiritual life and morality are based upon divine revelation which retains its integrity above and beyond the mechanisms of man's adaptive strategies vis-à-vis his environment. For these reasons, theologians and humanists generally have been reluctant even to consider the intimate relationships that obtain between biological development and spiritual and moral life.

This traditional abhorrence of the suggestion that moral and spiritual phenomena possess biological significance stands in need of reassessment today. The distinction between psychic events of morality and religion and the physical events of biological evolution is called seriously into question by the current affirmation (represented in this volume by Professor Steward) that biological and socio-cultural phenomena reside in one single continuum. The universal insight that man has transmuted the evolutionary process by means of his learned cultural patterns and that the most significant evolutionary response to our world is taking the form of cultural change—this insight forces us to recognize that the "higher" activities of man in his moral and spiritual life fulfill the same basic goal that his biological development served: man's most meaningful placement in his world.

It is possible to suggest that moral and spiritual phenomena play the role of achieving man's meaningful placement in his world without thereby denigrating that integrity of moral and spiritual realities, and without falling prey to a reductionism. This possibility is opened up for us now because we understand that the moral and the spiritual are realities appropriate to the particular level of complexity which life has reached in man. Thus, one can say that morality is possible only in a creature who has developed sufficiently, as man has, to be able to make choices. Or, one can say with Hudson Hoaglund (relying upon the thought of C. H. Waddington) that ethical systems are necessary in the evolutionary development of man, because "Human culture . . . is based on a mechanism that requires people to be brought up in such a way that they accept beliefs given them by others, such as parents and other influential persons in authority." To recognize in this way that man's spiritual life in ethics has an evolutionary "place" is not to diminish moral life, but rather to understand its full significance more clearly.

Similarly, anthropologists and historians have recognized that at the level of complexity at which life is lived in human societies, religious belief and behavior constitute a response to the world which no previous form of life could undertake, simply because no previous form was sufficiently sensitive to the world to make religion and other forms of spiritual life meaningful. Theodosius Dobzhansky, in his recent *The Biology of Ultimate Concern*, develops an impressive thesis that the awareness of death and religion, which do not serve directly as adaptive devices in man's development, are nevertheless inescapable concomitants to self-awareness which *does* serve the adaptive purpose of organizing and integrating the physical and mental capacities by means of which man controls his environment.

All of these concrete suggestions find their theoretical

foundation in the theory that the realm of *Geist*, the spiritual life of man which includes his culture and morality, is in some sense a *phase* of the development of life. This theory rests upon an ontological model which acknowledges levels or dimensions of organization within reality, from inanimate matter up through human culture. Pierre Teilhard de Chardin has given this mode of thinking a particularly forceful expression in his insistence that the realm of spiritual and moral phenomena is the intensely complex phase of biological evolution into which it appears to be the natural destiny of matter to evolve. It is their *complexity* and *structure* that differentiate the spiritual phenomena from "lower" forms of life, a complexity which is marked by self-awareness, moral sensitivity, cultural achievement, religion, and other characteristics. The phenomena of man's spirit are thus seen in their full biological significance as playing a role at the apex of life as it has evolved so far. These phenomena are neither reductionistically subsumed under the mechanisms of natural selection nor ascribed to some mysterious and unnecessary life force. Rather, they are seen as the types of activity appropriate to life that has reached the complexity of human culture. In this manner, we can understand on the one hand that spiritual phenomena are necessary for the sustaining of the evolutionary process, and on the other hand that the natural destiny of evolution, given the development toward complexity that seems apparent, is to move in the direction of the phase of complexity that we call spirit. There is indeed a sense in which man's morality and religion are part of man's adaptive response to his environment—that is one half of the story. The other half is that, given our world and the process of life, man's morality and religion, and culture, the development of natural phenomena is incomplete apart from a larger destiny which includes the spiritual dimensions of the life process. Whether these "spiritual" dimensions make the claim of humanism, to be rooted in man's distinctive sensibilities, or the claim of religion, to be grounded in a divine ground, they stand both as an ultra-refinement of man's response to his world and as the (up to this point) crowning destiny of the evolutionary process.

The Relationship of Spirit and Matter

A host of philosophical and theological problems arise when we attempt to define more closely the two terms that figured so prominently in the previous section, spiritual phenomena and the phenomena that are customarily referred to under the term "matter" or "nature." Here we can consider three relationships which seem to have been approached in parallel fashion: spirit and matter, mind and body, man and nature. Evolutionary theory and the work of the biologists generally has called new attention to the relationship of these pairs, both because of its over-all insistence that the "higher" form in each pair is intimately related to the lower, since it has evolved from that lower form, and also because of its renewed study of the precise mechanisms of interrelationship between each form of these pairs.

Ian Barbour has developed four categories of analysis in this problem that serve us well: dualistic views, reductionistic views, "two-aspect" views and a metaphysical view which focuses on the continuum of levels, as we suggested in the previous section.

The dualistic view, which sharply separates spirit from matter, mind from body, and man from nature stems philosophically (in modern times at least) from Cartesian thought with its dichotomies between body and mind and theologically from a tendency that was first embodied in Hellenistic Christian thought, which denigrated the material realm, holding that the spirit's destiny was to escape from the prison of the body. Theologically, this separation was taken to its extreme by the Gnostics, who considered material to be the product of a defective sexual relationship between two of the divine beings. Although this dualism is foreign to the authentic Christian tradition, it has been a simple matter to read the biblical materials and to interpret them dualistically. Such interpretations emphasize the dualism between spirit and flesh, and they exalt the uniqueness of man as a spiritual creation over against the world of nature. This dualistic view was given impetus through Augustine's theology in the West, and it has persisted in Existentialist philosophies and theologies. Scientifically and philosophically, the dualistic view of body and mind has had many adherents. In this volume Professor Holmer seems to represent this point of view. One great problem confronting the proponents of this view is that of accounting for the interaction of two entities so dissimilar as body and mind.

Reductionist views are of two kinds: those which consider mind and spirit to be epiphenomena, in a view that is not far from materialism, and those who subscribe to behaviorism, as J. B. Watson and B. F. Skinner have done in such celebrated fashion. Gilbert Ryle has given philosophical elaboration to the position, in a modified form, by insisting that the dimension of mind can be reduced to statements of disposition. In both its scientific and philosophical expressions, reductionistic views refuse to allow an integrity to the realm of mind and spirit. One of the perennial concerns of humanists and theologians has been the tendency of certain sciences (particularly molecular biology, which studies the physical-chemical processes of life) to attempt to reduce all of life, including man, to the smallest possible particles and thus subject them to the criteria that are appropriate to matter.

The "two aspect" theories (to use Barbour's phrase) attempt to preserve the integrity of both members of the pairs mind/body and man/nature (and presumably this could be applied to spirit/matter also) by suggesting that, as Herbert Feigl puts it, "Instead of conceiving of two realms or two concomitant types of events, we have only one reality which is represented in two different conceptual schemes." This sets the dualism back into the realm of language, rather than in reality itself. "Mind-language" and "body-language" are two ways of speaking of the same reality; the former speaks from the self-awareness of the existing person, the latter, from the observations of the scientist who cannot step into that self-awareness. Hans Jonas also underlines the existence of these two spheres, calling them the "vitalistic-inward" and the "physical-outward" perspectives. The modesty of this proposal and its ability to obviate dualism and reductionism make it attractive. It still does not answer, however, the question of what reality must be like in order to give rise to these two aspects.

As we indicated earlier, however, there is a large body of evolutionary thought, or thought that has been influenced by evolutionary modes of thinking, which prefers to locate the members of our three pairs in a continuum of levels or dimensions of reality. This body of opinion, represented by such diverse thinkers as Teilhard de Chardin on the one hand and Whitehead and Alexander on the other, insists that the members of the pairs coexist with each other, that the "higher" member has emerged *through* a continuum which includes the "lower" member, and that in a sense the "higher" member—whether mind, spirit, or man—is to be understood as the distinctive structure or configuration which is appropriate to the extremely complex level of the advanced levels of development. Thus, "mind" is the structure which body forms at a certain complex level; or, "spirit" is the structure which material reality has assumed at certain levels of complexity. This view insists that the higher member of each pair is indeed distinctive, while at the same time insisting that the lower member is ineradicably part of the pre-history of that higher distinctive form. The Roman Catholic theologian and philosopher Karl Rahner expresses this view in "Christianity within an Evolutionary View of the World" in volume five of *Theological Investigations*:

> If man is thus the self-transcendence of living matter, then the history of Nature and spirit forms an inner, graded unity in which natural history develops towards man, continues in him as *his* history, is conserved and surpassed in him and hence reaches its proper goal with and in the history of the human spirit.

Teilhard espouses a similar position, in his concepts of geosphere, biosphere, and noosphere—each referring to a more complex phase of the continuum.

This last view, the "metaphysics of levels," tackles the question left unanswered by the other views, namely, the nature of the reality which has manifested both mind *and* body, spirit *and* matter, man *and* nature. It harks back to the unitary view of man which seems most deeply embedded in the biblical view of man and spirit and body. Moreover, this "metaphysics of levels" holds particular importance for our general picture of man. Indeed, this is a topic which deserves further comment.

Weston La Barre, the anthropologist, once said that "evolution is life learning about matter (or what amounts to the same thing, matter learning purposes)." Karl Rahner has written: We must "try to see man as the being in whom the basic tendency of matter to find itself in the spirit by self-transcendence arrives at the point where it definitely breaks through." Now as diverse as the authors of these two quotations are, they both share in one common assumption, an assumption that must be accepted today as part of the intellectual consensus among thinking men, whether they be scientists or theologians, Christians or non-Christians: namely, that man can no longer be set off against the natural or material realm as an absolutely new and unique creature, but rather, he is a part of nature, one specific configuration of nature. Biochemistry and genetics reveal to us that each individual's *internal* development, from conception on, is molded by and composed of the earthy materials of life. Paleontologists, anthropologists, and ecologists remind us that man is inextricably a part of the nature that has preceded him and which surrounds him.

Although this conception of man as a part of nature's continuum precedes the nineteenth century, there is probably no single intellectual force that impressed it more permanently in the contemporary self-consciousness than the theory of evolution, which charts the kinship of all of life, from simplest organisms to man.

As commonplace as this assertion of man's relatedness to nature is, there is still much to be reshaped in Western philosophy and theology, if they are to take the current picture of man seriously. Philosophical modes of thought which (like existentialism) have turned the Kantian preoccupation with human consciousness into a cause for opposing man and nature must be reassessed. Similarly, theological conceptions which separate nature and human spirit, which identify man with inner intentionality that is sharply set off against his "works" in the world, which identify the image of God in man solely with his mind or intellect—these, too, must be reshaped considerably. Indeed, there is an entire range of contemporary sensibility which has failed to understand that the range of being from material nature to man, from one-celled organisms to man's creative spirit, is a continuum that can be understood only ecologically. Technology which fails to consider its impact on the natural world, and ultimately on man; anti-conservationist movements; and groups that are insensitive to the need for genuine urban renewal are typical of widespread thinking in our society

which does not fully understand the consensus which underlies this "metaphysics of levels," the conception that
matter and spirit, mind and body, man and nature are in
a continuum, in which what we call "higher" realities and
functions are to be understood as distinctive and complex configurations of the "lower."

The enterprise of placing man (and spirit and mind)
in his proper reciprocal relationship within the continuum
of nature involves, finally, accepting the constant factor
of change that characterizes that nature. Indeed, one of
Darwin's chief insights was that a theory of nature must
take change into account. We will focus attention more
fully on change in a later section of this essay, but it
should be noted here that placing man in the context of
a *changing* nature makes it all the more difficult for us
to determine what the proper definition of humanity is,
what is the *peculiarity* of *human* nature. Much of the
previous philosophical and theological tradition has insisted that there is some sort of "essence" which characterizes the human self, some "essence" that is distinc-
tively and irrevocably "human." The social psychologist
Erving Goffman has described this as the point of view
that conceives of the self "as something housed within
the body of its possessor, especially the upper parts
thereof, being a nodule, somehow, in the psychobiology
of personality." Theologically, this concern for man's essence has resulted in the conviction that human nature
has not really changed since Adam's creation. It remains
to be seen how theological understandings of grace, sin,
and justification will be reshaped by an adequate appreciation of man's placement within a continuum of
changing nature. Goffman, as well as biological exponents of evolution and psychologists, insist that the self
is not only not a solid, given entity, but that it emerges
out of the involvement and interaction which the individual experiences in his world. If the "essential" self is
constituted by involvement in the world, then in what

sense can "works" be said to be secondary to the justification and redemption of self? This is just one of the pressing new questions that the theological tradition faces, partly on account of the impetus given by evolutionary thinking.

Philosophy and theology will not want to stop talking about the human self and its distinctiveness within the continuum of nature, but the basic questions concerning the definition of "nature," "life," and "man" himself must be reopened, in light of the new consensus symbolized by the "metaphysics of levels," and the picture of man which it suggests.

Freedom and Determinism

The issue of whether freedom or determinism characterizes reality, or more specifically in this context whether man is free or determined, is as old as human thought itself. Biology and evolutionary theory have entered importantly into the discussion of this issue, because (in alliance with scientific explanation generally) they have studied man's origins and the mechanisms of his behavior so as to frame hypotheses which account for his behavior. The two most forceful aspects of current biological thinking in this regard are the theory of *natural selection,* which invites us to consider man as bound to his environment, able only to respond to its challenges and to initiate nothing on his own, and *genetic theories,* which seem to some to indicate that fortune has cast her dice, compelling the individual to fulfill the destiny that is written in his genetic composition from conception to death. Although both of these assertions—man's captivity to his environment and genetic destiny—have made a deep impact in our thinking, both of them are open to serious question, and both open up the immensely complex questions that attend the issue of freedom and determinism.

It is helpful to remember that much hinges on how one defines the terms "freedom" and "determinism." At least three important distinctions must be made in defining these terms.

(a) There is the classical point of view which holds that freedom is man's *autonomy*, the power to initiate courses of action on his own and control the outcome of that action. Under this view, anything less than autonomy is evidence for a deterministic view. At times, Saint Augustine, Luther, and Calvin seem to have argued in this manner, and their argumentation has been almost determinative for much of the Western theological tradition. The argument for autonomy does indeed seem to be easily refuted, in light of all the forces which countermand man's ability to initiate and sustain his own courses of action. Professor Gilkey's article stands within this Augustinian position.

(b) On the opposite extreme, there is the position which identifies freedom with indeterminacy. The celebrated Heisenberg Uncertainty Principle, or Principle of Indeterminacy, calls attention to the fact that certain experimental measurements simply cannot be performed with accuracy; for example, that it is experimentally impossible to measure *both* the velocity and position of an electron, although either can be measured independently. This phenomenon has engendered much speculation among scientists, philosophers, and theologians. Four interpretations seem to have crystallized: (1) Those which consider the indeterminate factor to be simply a result of ignorance at the present time; these men steadfastly refuse to grant that indeterminacy is in fact real. (2) Those who understand uncertainty as rooted in experimental inadequacies. (3) Those who consider uncertainty to be rooted in nature itself, objectively. This point of view questions whether the concept of "object" is even adequate to nature, since that nature so obviously defies our attempts to study it in object-form. Several theologians have built upon this view of indeterminacy. (4) Those interpretations which consider both "indeterminism" and "determinism" to be "fruitful maxims" or "regulative principles" for inquiry, rather than objective descriptions of nature. Indeterminism and determinism in this view become characteristics of man's cognition, which are valuable so long as they resolve problems. This position is related to Barbour's "two language" analysis, which understands freedom as characteristic of an agent's own description of his action of choice, whereas determinism characterizes an outside observer's description of that same action. The chief difficulty with all of these conceptions is that indeterminacy, in any form, seems to be too cautious a term to identify with freedom. Indeterminacy affirms little more than that *chance* is at work in the world, or that potentiality for unexpected behavior is a reality. Can one explain the development of life through the processes of natural selection simply by chance? Does the affirmation of this chance factor of contingency do justice to what man means by freedom?

(c) Another definition of freedom and determinism identifies them with ability or inability to find *antecedents* for any given behavior. This point of view is really much more devastating than either of the views previously considered. It is not really the concept of chance or autonomy which most affects man's understanding of his freedom. Rather, man's freedom is undercut by the knowledge that certain genetic and psychological antecedents may be present in his life which predispose him toward certain lines of behavior, whether he is cognizant of these antecedents or not, and that he has had absolutely no choice over these antecedents. Closely related to this argumentation are the notions that it is not so much a question of whether behavior has discernible antecedents, since indeed *all* behavior does have such antecedents, but whether the behavior is *compelled* or not, and whether the agent did have the possibility to behave differently if he had wished. This concern for the freedom to choose between alternatives approaches the thinking of biologist Theodosius Dobzhansky, who has argued that man's genetic endowment is not to be considered as the "dice of destiny," thrown to determine his behavior in detail, but rather that it provides man with a wide range of possibilities to respond to a variety of environments. This diversity is, in Dobzhansky's thinking, the "biological basis of human freedom." One might ask, however, whether diversity of alternatives is an adequate basis for freedom, since it too fails to consider the genetic and psychological factors which so *predispose* an individual that he cannot judge adequately between the alternatives, but must rather choose one compulsively in disregard of his other theoretical options.

However one defines freedom and determinism, evolutionary theory challenges Christian faith to refine its understanding of the issues, in order to clarify man's relation to the determining power of his genetic and cultural heritage. Moreover, there is the question of how this genetic and cultural heritage is related to God's providential "determinism." Christians have been able to assert man's freedom (almost autonomy) when determinisms of fate or economic and political forces seemed to undercut his ability to appropriate the freedom of sonship in grace (St. Paul, Origen). But on the other hand, Christians have also been able to humble man when the consciousness of freedom seemed to blind him to his dependence upon God. Theologians as varied as Augustine, Calvin, Schleiermacher, and H. R. Niebuhr have interpreted the Christian faith as a kind of determinism, focusing upon God's determinism as the foundation of man's existence.

The Relationship of God to Nature

One of the most scandalous features of evolutionary theory for Christians in Darwin's time was the (supposed) implication that God's intimate relationship to the world, as its Creator, was threatened by the notion that natural evolutionary causes could explain the world and man. For this reason, the impact of Darwin is closely tied to that of Lyell and the geologists who accounted for the physical world in terms of gradual natural processes. Newman Smyth and his colleagues were quick to remind their more cautious coreligionists that evolution could be conceived as "God's way of doing things" (to use a phrase of John Fiske's). As a consequence, they turned much of their effort to reinterpreting the Genesis account of creation in terms of evolution.

Nevertheless, there are many indications that the philosophical and theological problems underlying God's relationship to the world in an evolutionary mode of thought are still unresolved. In an essay on evolution, Karl Rahner can still say that the chief question to be resolved is that of "God's presence in precisely *that* dimension where man feels himself at home and in which alone he feels himself competent, viz. in the world and not in heaven." Furthermore, we remember that one of the chief ecclesiastical objections to the evolutionary thinking of Teilhard de Chardin was the question, as Rahner puts it, of how to understand that novelty emerged in the natural world, as a result of finite things transcending themselves, according to their natural laws and yet also as a result of God's operation.

Even though theologians and scientists are much more sophisticated today in their talk about God than they were a century ago, one basic issue remains as knotty as ever: Evolutionary theory insists that whatever the source (or initiating agent) of the functions of our world (natural and human) is, it is fully united with or embedded within the intrinsic processes by which this world develops. The creation of man by God may be accepted, but that creation is inconceivable (and therefore meaningless) if it suspends the intrinsic pattern of evolutionary development in which man presumably has shared as he emerged into what we now call *human* being. Evolutionary theory insists that whatever the ways of God with man might be, they are incarnate within the natural functions of this world, and in this sense, they are immanent in this world. Theologians react almost instinctively against this phrasing of the question. At their most unappealing, theologians have constructed a "God of the gaps" who worked precisely at those points where human knowledge was lacking, exactly at those points of mystery where the immanent processes of this world's functioning were themselves unknown. At their more sophisticated, theologians could speak, as Thomas Aquinas did, of secondary causes, the finite causes of the material realm, through which the Ultimate Cause, God, effected his purposes. Evolutionary theory challenges Christians to affirm that God is in some sense *in what we do see and know*, rather than in the "gaps."

Christian theology has wrestled with this problem in several ways. In asserting the Providence of God, it has affirmed God's agency in the day-to-day functioning of this world and in human affairs. The affirmation of Providence is never far from the affirmations of pantheism and determinism. When Providence is affirmed within a framework that is primarily moral—say, Luther, Calvin, or Jonathan Edwards—it tends toward a determinism which undercuts the traditional Christian concern for moral responsibility and freedom. When Providence is asserted in a framework that is ontologically or mystically inclined—Friedrich Schleiermacher or Teilhard de

Chardin, for example—it tends toward pantheism. It would be an illusion, however, to think that because the unfortunate connotations of pantheism and determinism inevitably attach themselves to the affirmation of God's immanent presence in the world and its processes—that because of these dangers, the affirmation itself can be avoided or shunted aside. Evolutionary theory will not permit Christian faith to avoid this affirmation.

On the basis of the foregoing considerations, one must conclude that a Christian who insists on symbolizing his faith in terms of evolutionary theory will find the current talk about God's death strangely unhelpful. The point is, for this Christian, that there either is a God, whose agency is explicable within the evolutionary framework, or else there is not. The apparatus by which the existence of God is known and affirmed is enormously complex, balancing as it does intellectual, emotional, psychological, moral, and aesthetic factors (to mention only a few!), and existential certainty about God's existence or non-existence does waver, often amidst great pathos. But within the concern for the symbolism of faith and evolutionary modes of thought, talk about the "death" of God is only rhetoric. Dobzhansky's recent book, *The Biology of Ultimate Concern,* brings this clearly in view, since it speaks of the awareness of the ultimate (God) in terms that lend an objectivity to the discussion which is antithetical to the current talk about God's death. If Dobzhansky's thesis is correct, that death-awareness and the awareness of God are natural correlates to the developing complexity of man, then the affirmation of God and his working in the processes of this world are not subject to erosion by the passage of the generations. They may be rejected as illusion and projection of human needs, but they cannot, in any objective sense, be said to have once pertained and then "died."

Karl Rahner seeks to resolve the problem of relating

God to an evolving world by emphasizing that the destiny of this world is fulfilled only when the "absolute ground of reality becomes directly interior to that which is grounded by it." Christian tradition speaks of this interior presence of God in the finite world by means of its doctrine of Christ and his Incarnation. Rahner insists that the classical dogma of the Hypostatic Union of the divine and human natures in Jesus indicates that God has entered fully into the evolutionary process and that he has permitted it to receive his own self-communication to the point of transcending itself, that is, evolving toward its own highest goal. The world's own highest goal, however, is that goal which God has implanted within it, which is made real in a proleptic sense in Jesus. Rahner's way of handling this problem builds on the Thomistic pattern of positing God as the primary cause which does its work in and through all secondary causes.

Teilhard de Chardin, however, probably stands as the most forceful exponent of the point of view that God must be understood to be fully involved in the evolutionary process, guiding its destiny. His thinking follows a sacramental form, that is, he conceives that God is so fully incarnate in this world that the material forms of this world are transparent to the divine presence that is in them. He could thus speak of the "Mass of the world," in which he conceived of the sacramental bread of the Holy Communion as a symbol that the entire world is the vehicle of Christ's presence. His master work of Christian spirituality, *The Divine Milieu*, brings this home with almost unbearable intensity:

> The more I examine myself, the more I discover this psychological truth: that no one lifts his little finger to do the smallest task unless moved, however obscurely, by the conviction that he is contributing infinitesimally (at least indirectly) to the building of something definitive—that is to say, to your work, my God.

This piety, which sees God's work in the activity of every "little finger" could also see the evolutionary work of God in war and in death, in which God is "painfully parting the fibres of my being in order to penetrate to the very marrow of my substance."

Theologians who have been influenced by so-called "process" metaphysics represent the most earnest Protestant efforts to formulate the intimate relation of God and his operation to the evolutionary processes of this world. Bernard Meland and Schubert Ogden are probably the most instructive examples of such theologians today. Although these two men differ in many ways in their thinking, both of them rely upon the metaphysical structure of James, Alexander, Hartshorne, and Whitehead in order to conceive of God as integral to the very matrix from which this world and its life emerges. God is therefore not to be found so much in "otherness" from this world as within its depths. Meland and Ogden provide the explicit philosophical structure in which many of Teilhard's assertions become intelligible, as Barbour's essay in this volume argues.

All of these theologians who have attempted to work with evolution as a hypothesis which can also pertain to the working of God in the world have had to defend themselves against two charges—the charge that they have fallen into the trap set by pantheism, which makes God indistinguishable, in the final analysis, from the world, and the charge that they have so closely associated God's will with the evolutionary course of life that they have overlooked the power and malignancy of evil (the very point on which Newman Smyth foundered). These theologians are well aware of these charges, and each in his own way has attempted to extricate himself from criticism. Whatever one may judge about the adequacy of their efforts, it does appear that theological and philosophical efforts to involve God intimately within the evolutionary process are inherently susceptible to the danger of making the differentiation between God and world more ambiguous than seems appropriate and thereby they give the appearance of taking evil less seriously than our experience warrants. In the long run, however, one might judge that this susceptibility is the price one has to pay for the more important value of relating God to the world of evolutionary processes in a manner that is intellectually viable.

Change as Constitutive of Reality

The theory of evolution was a brilliant hypothesis by means of which Charles Darwin was able to account for the amazing change and diversity which he encountered in his observations of living forms—change and diversity within species as well as between different species. When Christians today seek to think through their faith anew within evolutionary modes of thought, and when they try to symbolize their faith in evolutionary terms, they must inevitably come to terms with the bare fact of change and diversity which evolution implies. Evolutionary theory forces us to recognize that change is constitutive of physical and biological life, just as it is in the realm of history and man's self-consciousness. Therefore, if Christians conceive of themselves as God's creation under the forms of evolution, and if they are to understand God as intimately involved in the ongoing career of his creation, then the Christian understanding both of God and of man (as well as the rest of creation) must embrace change. The current intellectual climate is already predisposed to understand change and diversity under the rubrics of relativity, subjectivity of cognition, and the historical character of reality. Evolutionary theory extends the scope of that change and relativity even further.

Professor Steward speaks very forcefully of change in

is contribution to this conversation, and he states flatly that change is perhaps the chief value in our culture today. In my own contribution, I point to the impact of change on the Christian views of God and man, items that can bear elaboration here. One of the most important developments in recent theology is the effort by many hands to understand change—and even development—within God himself. It is impossible to avoid positing change and development in God when one has once allowed that God is involved in the development of a world that operates under the hypothesis of evolution. It is impossible to elaborate here the subtlety and complexity of these theological developments. It is enough to recognize that a concept of God is being fashioned in our own day which makes it possible for us to think through rigorously our Christian faith in evolutionary terms.

Evolution challenges the assumption that many theological (and non-theological, as well) views of man accept without question: namely, that man has not changed essentially since his creation by God. Evolution forces us to come to terms with the fact that man as species undergoes change, and will undergo change in the future, and that every individual man experiences change of a significant nature within himself. It is extremely difficult for us to imagine change in the species of man itself. Father Teilhard is one of the few who articulated his understanding of this change. He spoke of this change in terms of a Point Omega toward which man's ever increasing complexification is tending. The intense mystical dimension of this concept makes it difficult to work with, but even apart from his mysticism, this concept of Omega dramatizes Teilhard's conviction that evolution is able to make fresh starts within a species, when a maximum of complexification has reached the apparent end of its usefulness. He uses the image of a space vehicle which achieves one orbit, only to launch a second vehicle into a still higher orbit. Man's evolution has reached such a preliminary height, and now that his society is global and cybernated, man can develop in a new orbit. Says Father Teilhard in his *Man's Place in Nature:* "We must distinctly and once and for all finish with the legend that continually crops up again of an earth that has, in man and with the man we now see, reached the limit of its biological potentialities." As I indicate in a later chapter, the practical advances of bio-technology, in concert with the theoretical assertions of evolutionary theory, compel us to recognize that man himself changes, and that our concept of man must incorporate this category of change.

The fact of change within each individual's career through life, both physically and psychically, as well as within his own self-consciousness implies that the self is a febrile thing, and that it is inseparable from the social and physical context in which it finds itself. Evolutionary theory shatters any concept of a static self, with its assertion of natural selection, that is, that the self becomes what it is in the effort to place itself satisfactorily within its world. Consideration of the cultural dimension of evolution focuses our attention on the social character of the environment in which the individual develops and adapts, and the essential dependence of each individual upon the social context in which he lives. Each man's selfhood is given to him by the social context, with the clear implication that the self changes, that it is febrile, in positive correlation to the social context in which it lives. Philosophical and theological conceptualities of man have only begun to take the implications of this interior change diversity seriously.

The upshot of evolutionary theory is that change is not epiphenomenon, but rather constitutive of reality at its physical and biological origins. Christians who claim that evolutionary theory is useful in the symbolization of their faith will find that one of its challenges is the successful incorporation of change into their formulations of belief and practice.

Conclusion

I indicated at the outset that the chapters in this volume make up a conversation. Conversations do not often run smoothly, without interruption, disagreement, or breaks in the train of thought. Indeed, the value of a conversation (as Martin Buber has taught us) is that each *Gespraechspartner* contributes what is in him, in some sort of reference to the other members of the conversational group.

It will be obvious from the following chapters that the philosophical-theological issues outlined in this introduction are far removed from the minds of some of the conversationalists represented in this book. Indeed, these issues appear pale, abstruse, and even lifeless, when placed alongside the passion which some of the other conversationalists display in their concern for the ethical crises that contemporary biology and evolutionary theory have unleashed.

I have no desire to dampen the ardor for these ethical issues. In fact, I would argue that the heat of these life-and-death issues always deserves priority over the abstract analysis of philosophical reflection. Nevertheless, it should be clear that even the most passionate of the responses in this volume are based, perhaps unknowingly, on philosophical and theological presuppositions which must be examined if ethical insight is to be properly disciplined and applied. To illustrate, we make the following observations, pertinent to each of the themes discussed above:

1) Our use of the fruits of bio-technology in the years ahead to enhance our lives, whether as simple as water fluoridation or as complex as genetic controls, will betray

very quickly whether we look upon these technical advances as antithetical to, concomitant with, or the fulfillment of the spiritual dimensions of mankind. Our ability or inability to make this technology a useful servant for man may rest on our corresponding willingness or unwillingness to relate spirit and nature constructively. Our wholeness as men depends on successfully effecting this relationship.

2) The morale of our society in the generations ahead will be decisively shaped by our ability to understand the meaning of freedom today, and our ability to communicate that understanding to the large masses of people. If we fail to conceptualize man's freedom adequately, we shall simply encourage the already widespread conviction that freedom can be preserved only by the rejection of the new automated and cybernated era in favor of a more comfortable illusion concerning the past. Or, a failure to understand the proper relation of freedom and determinism may encourage our people to entertain false hopes of what bio-technology and other advances in knowledge can accomplish. If we fail altogether to appreciate man's freedom in the midst of the determining factors of nature, we may demoralize ourselves completely.

3) The valuation Christians place on the contemporary world of science and technology, whether biological or other, is determined very largely by our ability to relate these movements to God's own will. The work of contemporary theologians to frame a concept of God that permits us to understand his intimate involvement in our world is encouraging; it makes possible the survival of faith in a secularist age. But we cannot overlook the large numbers of Christians who do not meaningfully relate God and the contemporary course of events. Christian participation in reasonable policy decisions to implement biological advances depends on the success Christians have in relating God and nature. It may also

be that the Christian contribution to the common life of all men today similarly depends on the resolution of this philosophical-theological issue.

4) The life of the churches and of our society in general will be determined in the years ahead by the ability of men-and-women-in-the-street to understand that change cannot be resisted successfully, that it is rooted in the very being of things, and the real challenge that faces us is what *kind* of change we will advance. If these men and women can understand their own human nature as constituted by change and accommodation, they will certainly be predisposed to much more creative and constructive policies in the era that will be marked by advances in bio-technology and other technologies.

These observations indicate that the abstractness and abstruseness of philosophical-theological analysis cannot be ignored, except at our own loss. Ethical passion and theoretical analysis must go together in the formulation and reformulation of the policies that will make the fruits of biology and evolutionary theory available for the health of our society.

EVOLUTION: BASIC TO BIOLOGY

A summary of evolutionary theory and some pertinent questions about man-made ways to control evolution.

WILLIAM T. KEETON

In the years since 1859, when Charles Darwin published *The Origin of Species*, the theory of evolution has come to be accepted as one of the most important unifying principles in biology. The general validity of the theory is no longer seriously questioned by biologists. And even the churches, many of which once felt threatened by it, have (with a few minor exceptions) come to realize that, instead of destroying anything fundamental to their faith, the theory may actually give them new insight into the nature of life and of man. Still, our modern understanding of evolution (and of inheritance, upon which evolution depends) raises some questions of great importance to our civilization, questions with which men must grapple in the years ahead. My purpose here is to present a summary of evolutionary theory as a point of departure for discussion of some of those questions in the articles to follow.

Darwin's theory consisted of two major parts: the concept of evolutionary change and the concept of natural selection. First, Darwin rejected the notion that living creatures are the immutable products of a sudden cre-

Dr. Keeton is an associate professor of biology at Cornell University, Ithaca, New York. Portions of his article are based on passages in his book *Biological Science* (© copyright 1967 by W. W. Norton and Company, all rights reserved).

ation, that they exist now in precisely the form in which they have always existed. He declared that change is the rule, that the organisms living today have descended by gradual changes from ancient ancestors quite unlike themselves. Second, Darwin said that natural selection is the guiding factor determining the course of the change. This guiding factor can be understood in completely mechanistic terms; no conscious purpose or design need be invoked. Let us examine the two parts of Darwin's theory separately.

The Concept of Evolutionary Change

To people living in the mid-20th century, the idea that lineages of organisms change with time seems far from revolutionary. We are used to change. We should probably be surprised to find anything that remained the same for any long period of time. But in Darwin's day things moved more slowly. The idea of a world in constant flux had few adherents. The vast majority accepted without question the notion that the universe was created a few thousand years before the birth of Christ, and that all species were put on the earth at that time and perpetuated themselves without change ever since. What sorts of evidence could Darwin bring forward to combat this static view?

First, he could point to the fossils, which indicated that forms of life different from those known today inhabited the earth in past ages. This is a point now familiar to grade-school children, who are aware that dinosaurs once roamed the earth in vast numbers but that one never sees dinosaurs nowadays. In museums they see dioramas of ancient seas filled with strange fish and shelled creatures unlike anything living today. They learn about the cavemen who, though clearly human, were clearly different from modern men in many ways. To us the existence of fossils seems convincing evidence that life on earth has been marked by change.

Second, Darwin could point to resemblances between living species. The forelimbs of a variety of mammals, for example, have essentially the same bones arranged in the same order; the basic bone structure of a man's arm, a dog's front leg and a seal's flipper is the same. Even a bird's wing shows the same bones. True, the size and shape of the individual bones vary from species to species, and some bones may be missing entirely in one or another species, but the basic construction is unmistakably identical. To Darwin, the resemblance suggested that all these species had descended from a common ancestor from whom each had inherited, with distinctive modifications, its forelimb. The fact that some species possess, in reduced and nonfunctional form, structures that in other species have important functions further convinced Darwin of the validity of his theory. Why would the Creator have given pigs, which walk on only two toes per foot, two other toes that dangle useless well above the ground? Why would he have given human embryos gill pouches and well developed tails only to make these disappear again before birth? It seemed much simpler to assume that such structures were inherited vestiges of structures that functioned in ancestral forms and that still function in other species descended from the same ancestor.

Third, and particularly convincing, Darwin could point to changes produced in domesticated plants and animals. How could anyone doubt that great changes can, with time, take place in organisms, when he has before him the historical evidence of the changes in domesticated forms? Where were French poodles and Mexican Chihuahuas 2,000 years ago? Where were Guernsey cattle and Leghorn chickens? Where were the modern strains of tomatoes and corn and roses? Their ancestors existed, but those ancestors bore little resemblance to poodles or Chihuahuas or Guernseys or Leghorns or garden tomatoes, corn, and roses. Obviously, radical changes have occurred in a few thousand, or even a few hundred, years. The ancestors of the poodles and Chihuahuas were wolves. The ancestors of modern corn were small wild plants with ears less than an inch long. Let anyone who would still insist that species cannot change explain these facts.

The Concept of Natural Selection

It was easy for Darwin to see that evolutionary change had occurred. But it took him many years to figure out what caused the changes. His first clue came from the breeding of domesticated plants and animals. When pigeon breeders, for example, are developing a new strain, they exploit the variation always seen among individuals by selecting the ones best endowed with the characteristics they want to propagate and using them as the parents of the next generation. So in each successive generation: the individuals that most nearly approximate the desired type are selected as breeders, and individuals that deviate markedly from the desired type are eliminated. After many generations of such selection, the pigeons will be very different from the ones the breeders began with. Since individual variation occurs in all populations of wild organisms, just as in populations of domesticated ones, Darwin reasoned that evolutionary change in these populations must be caused by some sort of natural selection of individuals with certain characteristics and elimination of individuals with other characteristics. But what sort of selective force might be at work in nature?

Consider for a moment a population of gray squirrels. If it is to be perpetuated at a stable level, each pair of squirrels must leave enough offspring to replace itself

—two, if we assume that all the offspring survive to reproduce. If the average number of progeny per pair were more than two, the population density would rise; if the average number were less than two, the population density would fall. Now, even a casual study of actual populations will reveal that the average number of offspring per pair is always more than two, usually far more. A single female frog may lay many thousands of eggs each year; a pair of gray squirrels usually has two litters per year, containing two to four young each; a single oak tree may produce millions of seeds during its lifetime. In short, very large reproductive potentials are the rule in all types of organisms. Yet natural populations never even approach the level that would be expected if all their progeny survived to reproduce. It is obvious, therefore, that a very high percentage of the young of any species fail to survive.

Once Darwin recognized this fact he had the clue he needed to explain natural selection. If survival of the young organisms were totally random—if each individual in a large population had exactly the same chance of surviving and reproducing as every other individual—then there would probably be little evolutionary change in the population. But survival and reproduction are never totally random. Some individuals are born with such gross defects that they stand almost no chance of surviving. And even among individuals not so severely afflicted, minor differences ensure that survival will not be totally random. In each generation, therefore, a slightly higher percentage of the well adapted individuals will leave progeny. If the characteristics are inherited, those favorable to survival will slowly become more common, and those unfavorable to it less common, as the generations pass. Given enough time, these slow shifts can produce major evolutionary changes.

Now let us compare the propagation of favorable characteristics in nature, as outlined above, with their propagation in domesticated organisms. In each case there is selection, by which we mean differential reproduction. In the breeding of domesticated plants and animals, the selection (differential reproduction) results from the deliberate choice of the breeder. In nature the selection (differential reproduction) results simply from the fact that individuals with different inherited characteristics have unequal chances of surviving and reproducing. Both sorts of selection, artificial and natural, cause some inherited characteristics to become more prominent in the population and others to become less so as the generations pass. Note that individuals, once born, are not changed by selection. An individual cannot evolve. The change is in the makeup of the population.

One difference between natural and artificial change should be noted; namely, the rate of the change. Breeders can practice very rigorous selection, eliminating all undesirable individuals in every generation and allowing only a few of the most desirable to reproduce. They can thus produce very rapid change. Natural selection is usually much less rigorous. Some poorly adapted individuals manage to survive and reproduce, and some well adapted individuals are eliminated. Hence evolutionary change is usually rather slow; major changes may take many thousands or even millions of years.

In summary: Darwin's explanation of evolutionary change in terms of natural selection depends on five basic assumptions: (1) Many more individuals are born in each generation than will survive and/or reproduce. (2) There is variation among individuals; they are not identical in all their characteristics. (3) Individuals with certain characteristics have a better chance of surviving and reproducing than individuals with other characteristics. (4) At least some of the characteristics resulting in differential reproduction are heritable. (5) Enormous spans of time are available for slow, gradual change. All the known evidence supports the validity of these five assumptions.

The Lamarckian View of Evolution

Darwin's theory of evolution by natural selection was one of two principal scientific interpretations of evolution proposed during the past century. The other was the hypothesis of evolution by the inheritance of acquired characteristics—an old and widely held idea often identified with Jean Baptiste de Lamarck, one of its more prominent supporters in the early 1800s.

According to the Lamarckian hypothesis, somatic characteristics acquired by an individual during its lifetime can be transmitted to its offspring. Thus the characteristics of each succeeding generation would be determined, in part at least, by all that happened to the members of the preceding generations, including modifications caused by experience, use and disuse of body parts, and accidents. Evolutionary change would be the gradual accumulation of such acquired modifications over many generations. The classic example (though now rather hackneyed) is the evolution of the long necks of giraffes. A Lamarckian view would be that ancestral giraffes with short necks frequently stretched their necks as much as they could to reach the tree foliage that constituted a major part of their food. This frequent neck stretching caused their offspring to have slightly longer necks. These, in turn, were stretched, so that the next generation had still longer necks. And so, as a result of neck stretching to reach higher and higher foliage, each generation had slightly longer necks than the preceding generation.

Contrasted with this Lamarckian hypothesis is the modern theory of natural selection. According to this theory, ancestral giraffes probably had short necks, but the precise length of the neck varied from individual to individual as a result of their slightly different genotypes. If the supply of food was somewhat limited, the longer-necked individuals had a better chance of surviving and leaving progeny than shorter-necked ones. This doesn't mean that all the shorter-necked individuals perished, nor that all the longer-necked ones survived to reproduce; it simply means that a slightly higher proportion of those with longer necks survived and left offspring. Hence the proportion of individuals with genes for longer necks increased slightly with each succeeding generation.

Despite the low opinion most modern biologists have of the hypothesis of evolution by inheritance of acquired characteristics, it was a logical and reasonable one when first proposed. In Lamarck's day (as in Darwin's) nothing was known about the mechanism of inheritance. Mendel had not yet performed his classic experiments on garden peas. It was therefore not illogical to assume that a change in any part of the body could be inherited. Even in ancient Greece it had been suggested that particles, or pangenes, from all parts of the body come together to form eggs and semen. This Greek idea of pangenesis would provide a hypothetical genetic basis for the Lamarckian hypothesis. If a long-distance runner built up his leg muscles, and if this development altered the pangenes from those muscles, then the runner's semen would include the altered pangenes and would confer on his children the larger leg muscles of their father.

A telling point against Lamarckianism is the refutation of the idea of pangenesis on which it depends. We now know that somatic cells do not affect the genotype of the germ cells—that immense alterations of the somatic cells can be performed without in any way influencing the hereditary information in the gametes (ova and sperms). We must conclude that the hypothesis of inheritance of acquired characteristics is no longer tenable.

Genetics and Evolutionary Theory

The rise of the science of genetics in the early part of this century gave a firm basis for Darwin's assumption of the heritability of adaptive traits. And it made possible the reformulation of Darwin's theory in terms of change in the gene pools of populations (the gene pool of a population is the sum total of all the genes possessed by all the individuals in the population). Suppose, for example, that a certain gene occurs in two allelic (reciprocal) forms, A and a, in a sexually reproducing population. Suppose, further, that A is much more common than a, the frequencies of the two alleles being 0.9 and 0.1 respectively. If those frequencies were to change with time, the change would be evolution. In short, evolution can be defined as change in gene frequencies (or genotype ratios) within gene pools. Therefore, we can determine what factors cause evolution by determining what factors can produce a shift in gene frequencies within a gene pool.

Persons first encountering the idea of evolution as a change in gene frequencies often assume that a more common allele (A in our example) will automatically increase in frequency while a less common allele (a) will automatically decrease in frequency and eventually be lost from the population. This assumption is incorrect. It can be shown mathematically that changes in gene frequencies are not automatic, that they occur only when something disturbs the genetic equilibrium of a population. This fact was first recognized in 1908 by G. H. Hardy and W. Weinberg, working independently. According to the so-called Hardy-Weinberg Law, under certain conditions of stability, both gene frequencies and genotype ratios remain constant from generation to generation in sexually reproducing populations.

Requirements for Equilibrium

What are the "certain conditions" that the Hardy-Weinberg Law says are necessary in order for the gene pool of a population to be in genetic equilibrium? These conditions are as follows: (1) The population must be large enough to make it highly unlikely that chance alone could significantly alter gene frequencies. (2) Mutations must not occur, or else there must be mutational equilibrium. (3) There must be no immigration or emigration. (4) Reproduction must be totally random.

In theory, a population would have to be infinitely large in order for chance to be completely ruled out as a causal factor in the changing of gene frequencies. In reality, of course, no population is infinitely large. For all practical purposes, however, many natural populations are large enough so that it is unlikely that chance alone could appreciably alter the gene frequencies in their gene pools. Any breeding population with more than 10,000 members of breeding age is probably not significantly affected by random change.

The second condition necessary for genetic equilibrium—either that there be no mutation or else that there be mutational equilibrium—is probably never met in any population. Mutations are always occurring, and there is no known way of stopping them. And rarely if ever is mutation in exact equilibrium. Thus mutation pressure will tend to cause a slow shift in the gene frequencies in the population. More stable alleles will tend to increase in frequency and more mutable alleles to decrease, unless some other factor offsets the mutation pressure. But despite the fact that mutation pressure is almost always present, it probably is seldom a major factor in producing changes in gene frequencies in a population. Mutation is so slow that, acting alone, it would take an enormous time to produce much change. Furthermore, mutation is random; it is frequently in a direction different from that in which other factors are causing the organism actually to evolve. Mutations increase variability and thus are the ultimate raw material of evolution, but they seldom determine the direction or nature of evolutionary change.

If a gene pool is to be in genetic equilibrium, it is obvious that there cannot be immigrants coming to it from other populations and introducing new genes. Nor can there be loss of genes from the gene pool by emigration. Probably, however, a high percentage of natural populations experience at least a small amount of gene migration, and this factor, which enhances variation, tends to upset Hardy-Weinberg equilibria. But there are doubtless populations that experience no gene migration, and in many instances where migration does occur it is probably so slight as to be essentially negligible as a factor in causing significant shifts in gene frequencies.

The fourth condition necessary for genetic equilibrium in a population is that reproduction be totally random. When biologists speak of reproduction in this context, they do not mean simply the mating process per se; rather, they mean everything that contributes in any way to the reproductive continuity of the population. This obviously includes a vast number of different factors: selection of a mate, physical efficiency and frequency of the mating process, fertility, total number of zygotes produced at each mating, percentage of zygotes that lead to successful embryonic development and birth, survival of the young until they are of reproductive age, fertility of the young, and even, in some cases, survival of postreproductive adults when their survival affects either the chances of survival or the reproductive efficiency of the young. Therefore, if reproduction is to be totally random, all these factors must be random; i.e., they must not be correlated with genotype. This condition is probably never met in any population; probably no aspect of reproduction is totally devoid of correlation with genotype. Nonrandom reproduction is the universal rule. And nonrandom reproduction, in the broad sense in which we have defined it here, is synonymous with natural selection. So we are saying here that natural selection is always operative in all populations.

In summary: of the four conditions necessary for the genetic equilibrium characterized by the Hardy-Weinberg Law, the first (large population size) is met reasonably often, the second (no mutation) is never met, the third (no migration) is met sometimes, and the fourth (random reproduction) is never met. Therefore, we conclude that complete equilibrium in a gene pool is not expected; that evolutionary change is a fundamental characteristic of the life of all populations, including human populations.

The Importance of Environment

The central role played by the environment in evolutionary phenomena should be obvious. There is no absolute scale that determines which genes are beneficial and which harmful. It is the context in which the genes occur that determines this. Thus selection pressure against the gene for sickle-cell anemia—a severe, usually fatal, disease—is intense in the United States, and consequently the gene is very infrequent. But in Africa the gene is much more frequent than one might expect, apparently because heterozygous carriers of the gene enjoy some immunity to malaria. In other words, in the African environment, where malaria is prevalent, the gene has a beneficial effect that partly balances its harmful effect. Another example is human skin pigmentation. Genes producing dark pigmentation are prevalent in nearly all populations living in or near the tropics; apparently the pigment helps prevent damage from the high incidence of ultraviolet radiation. The genes are much less frequent in populations living at northern latitudes, where the ultraviolet radiation is less intense.

The environment is important not only in determining the selection pressures acting on genes but also in helping control the expression of the traits determined by the genes. Thus fruit flies with the gene for vestigial wings have vestigial wings if they are reared at normal room temperatures, but if they are reared at temperatures as high as 88°F their wings are almost as long as normal. Human beings with genes for very large size will not grow large if raised on a starvation diet. In short, we do not inherit characters; we inherit only genes, only potentialities. Other factors govern whether or not the potentialities are realized. All organisms are products of both their inheritance and their environment. This fact is illustrated particularly well in studies on animal behavior.

Interaction of Inheritance and Learning

During the first half of this century, a controversy raged over the relative importance of inheritance and learning in animal behavior. Some psychologists, particularly those of the "white rat" school in America, went to the extreme of denying that inheritance plays any significant role in behavior. Such an attitude seemed incredible to biologists, familiar as they were with the nervous and effector systems of animals. Clearly, nervous pathways and effectors are inherited, and an animal can exhibit only those behavior patterns for which it has the appropriate neural and effector mechanisms. Furthermore, learning itself depends on inherited neural pathways: if the necessary connections are not there, no amount of experience can establish a given behavior pattern. But if the psychologists went to extremes in their emphasis on learning, many biologists studying animal behavior (they frequently call themselves ethologists) went to equal extremes in the other direction. They greatly exaggerated the role of inheritance in determining even the precise details of complex behavior patterns. Fortunately, much of the furor of this old "nature vs. nurture" controversy has subsided, and both psychologists and biologists increasingly recognize how fundamental both inheritance and learning are in determining the behavior of higher animals, and how inextricably intertwined are the contributions of these two elements in most behavior patterns. As in so many instances in the history of science, an insistence on an "either-or" approach proved unproductive.

One way of viewing the interaction of inheritance and learning in animal behavior is to consider inheritance as determining the limits within which a particular type of behavior can be modified and to consider learning as determining, within those limits, the precise nature of the behavior.

An example that dramatically illustrates the interaction of inheritance and learning is the song of the European chaffinch. W. H. Thorpe of the University of Cambridge raised chaffinches in isolation and found that such birds gave recognizable chaffinch calls but were unable to sing a normal chaffinch song. One might assume, therefore, that the call is inherited but that the song is not. But the matter is more complicated. Thorpe demonstrated that young chaffinches raised in isolation and permitted to hear a recording of a chaffinch song when about six months old would quickly learn to sing properly. But young chaffinches permitted to hear recordings of songs of other species that sing similar songs did not ordinarily learn to sing those other songs. Apparently chaffinches must learn to sing by hearing other chaffinches, but they have inherited the ability to recognize and respond most strongly to the songs of their own species. The inherited limits ordinarily preclude a chaffinch's learning a completely erroneous song. The songs of individual chaffinches differ slightly, and the differences are probably due, in part, to learning, but these differences are minor when compared to the differences between the songs of closely related species. Clearly, to ask whether chaffinch song is inherited or learned is to ask a meaningless question. The song is neither wholly inherited nor wholly learned; it is both inherited and learned. Chaffinches inherit the neural and muscular mechanisms responsible for chaffinch song, and they inherit, apparently, the ability to recognize a chaffinch song when they hear it, and they inherit severe limits on the type of song they can learn; but the experience of hearing another chaffinch sing is necessary to trigger their inherited singing abilities into action, and in this sense their song is learned.

Man's Role in Evolution

Man, by his unrivaled ability to alter his environment, is influencing in profound ways the evolution of all species with which he comes in contact. Thus there is evidence that in industrial areas a variety of moth species have evolved darker pigmentation that makes them less conspicuous against soot-covered tree trunks. Many species of insects have rapidly evolved new physiological and behavioral traits as a consequence of the intense selection pressure resulting from man's use of insecticides. Use of antibiotics has caused evolution of hardy new strains of bacteria. The clearing of forests for agricultural purposes has led to drastic decline in the population densities of some species and to increase of others. Long-established balances between prey species and their predators and parasites have been destroyed, often with far-reaching consequences for the entire ecosystem.

While a few of man's effects on his environment have been deliberately induced, most have been unintentional. But whether deliberately or unintentionally, man has precipitated a period of wholesale and rapid change unmatched since life began. Since disruption of the ecosystem will unavoidably increase as civilization expands, it behooves man to use his newly acquired knowledge and technology to try, as best he can, to control the change in ways that will benefit both his own species and the other organisms around him. Unthinking and greedy destruction cannot be tolerated if the future of life on earth is to be secure.

Man now has the ability to alter deliberately some aspects of the future evolution of his own species. Modern medicine, by saving people with gross genetic defects that would once have been fatal, permits perpetuation of genes that natural selection would formerly have eliminated. Should anything be done about this? Man could, if he chose, practice eugenics—deliberately restrict the perpetuation of some genetic traits and encourage that of others. And now that we have at last learned the genetic code (which is written in the structure of a chemical called deoxyribonucleic acid—DNA for short), the day will surely come (though probably not very soon) when genes can be altered in order to design, at least in part, new human beings. When that day comes, how do we decide what to design? And who decides? And who controls the one who decides? More pressing is the problem of regulating the size of human populations now that we have interfered with the action of many of the former regulating factors. Already some people are asking whether we should abandon our campaigns to eradicate malaria and other diseases, since there is little evidence that men will consent to the really effective population control measures that become ever more necessary as the traditional killers are vanquished.

These are important questions that are at one and the same time biological, economic, political and moral. They must be faced—soon. We have already gone too far toward modifying biological evolution to pull back now. Like it or not, the next few generations of human beings must answer these and many similar questions. The answers they give may well have as profound an influence on the future of life as anything that has happened since the first cells appeared in the primordial seas.

CULTURAL EVOLUTION TODAY

Although scientific analysis can point to causal factors of social change, it cannot provide criteria by which to assess what is good.

JULIAN H. STEWARD

A century ago, when anthropologists no longer felt constrained by the theory of special creation, they borrowed the term "evolution" to signify that, just as (according to the biologists) all physical life had developed from primordial forms, so all cultures had developed from primitive beginnings. In seeking to discover order in cultural development, however, they did not attempt to use Darwinian models.

Darwin based his evolutionary theory on Linnaeus' taxonomy of life forms, a treelike developmental scheme wherein limbs, branches and twigs represented diverging descendants of common ancestors. The cultural evolutionary taxonomy, however, was one of parallel stages, through which each society was assumed to evolve independently. The classic example of this concept, which is known as "unilinear evolution," is L. H. Morgan's sequence of savagery, barbarism, civilization (published in *Ancient Society* in 1877). Whereas the biologists explained evolution by such principles as the survival of the fittest, the 19th century anthropologists invoked the principle of progress—Victorian England being the acme of civilization.

Dr. Steward is research professor of anthropology at the University of Illinois, in Urbana.

Archaeological and ethnographic research during the present century has completely discredited the unilinear schemes because of the lack of empirical evidence, while a more scientific view rejected the principle of progress because it explained nothing. Within two decades ethnologists became preoccupied with "cultural relativism"—the analysis of each culture in terms of its uniqueness—while archaeologists concerned themselves with the sequence and distribution of culture elements. Cultural evolution was generally repudiated, and attempts to find causes for cultural phenomena were regarded as folly. Nevertheless, a tenuous interest in cultural evolution survived. The concept was revived in new form by the papers presented at several symposiums held in 1959 to celebrate the centennial of the publication of Darwin's *Origin of Species*.

Today the term "cultural evolution" is used in connection with the explanatory analysis of the development of particular cultures. The compulsion to create world schemes and discover universal principles has diminished. There are, however, those who still hold the conviction that anything labeled "evolution" ought to conform to some kind of social Darwinism and therefore strive to use biological analogies no matter how inappropriate they may be. Fortunately, the confusion of cultural and biological phenomena is being dissipated, and cultural evolution is beginning to develop its own methodology. This method, which includes what I designate "factor determination," can best be explained in connection with the substantive illustrations given below. It consists fundamentally of empirical analysis of individual cases, followed by cross-cultural tests of postulated cause-and-effect relationships.

I emphasize causality because any assumption that teleological or orthogenetic principles, divine intervention or free will are at work would nullify scientific explanation. To those who disagree I can only say that science must proceed *as if* natural laws operate consistently and without exceptions, as if all cultures and all aspects of human behavior had determinants—no matter how difficult the task of unraveling the intricately interrelated phenomena.

However, the nature of cultural evolution may be placed in perspective by answering the five questions that follow.

The Nature of Cultural Evolution

1. *What is the relationship between cultural evolution and biological evolution?* This fundamental question raises the issue of the relationship between man's biological and cultural characteristics during the course of past evolution as well as at the present time.

The nature of biological evolution was explained in the first article of this series. The evolution of manlike animals, or hominids, became distinctive only when the hominids developed culture, which thereafter became a factor in their biological evolution. As Darwin observed, man is a self-domesticated animal which depends on its culture as well as on its biological equipment to survive.

Over a period of a million years or so, the first hominids, or australopithecines, attained a posture sufficiently erect to allow them to become fairly mobile bipeds—in contrast to the quadrupedal apes—and to use their hands to make simple tools. Because their brains were little larger than those of the apes, their capacity for speech is doubtful and their potential for rational thought was limited. *Homo erectus,* who appeared perhaps half a million years ago, had brains intermediate in size between those of the apes and of modern men. He used fire, made a variety of tools and finally devised cultural means to live in cold climates. At least 40,000 years ago, evolution of the basic biological characteristics of modern man, *Homo sapiens*, was completed. Our ancestors had a completely erect posture, hands with opposable thumbs, fully developed brains and specialized cranial areas for speech, hearing, vision and association which are fundamental to language, memory and rational thought. In addition, the human infant undoubtedly underwent the long period of dependency which develops a bond between parents and offspring. However, although minor morphological changes continue, there is no evidence that man's inherent ability has increased.

2. *Is evolution now chiefly cultural?* Since no important biological change in *Homo sapiens* has occurred during the past 40,000 years, the tremendous evolutionary changes in culture within this period must have nonbiological explanations. The first modern men were fairly simple food hunters and collectors, but, owing to many cultural innovations, some men adapted to the glacial conditions of Europe while others adapted to more temperate climates. Different lines of cultural evolution began at that time.

Some 30,000 years later, the inhabitants of the Near East domesticated plants and animals and became settled farmers. At about the same time the American Indians, the first of whom migrated to the Western hemisphere only 20,000 or 30,000 years ago, domesticated native plants. By about 3,000 B.C. (5,000 years ago), the great cultural traditions or state civilizations of the Near East, India, China, Meso-America and the Andes had taken distinctive form. During the past few hundred years—less than one-fifth of one per cent of the time modern man has occupied the earth—the industrial revolution has transformed Euro-American culture and disseminated its influence throughout the world. But this incredible acceleration of cultural evolution and the emergence of many distinctive cultural traditions have had no effect on biological evolution.

The Question of Race

This brings us to the question of race, which, though irrelevant to cultural evolution, cannot be ignored owing to the spurious claims of racists and eugenicists. History discloses that cultural features have not only been transferred and diffused from one race or society to another on a massive scale, but that the centers of creativeness have shifted within and between races. As A. L. Kroeber showed in *Configurations of Culture Growth* (1944), the inherent ability of any population may remain latent until activated by appropriate stimulative circumstances. Civilization was first developed in the Near East, but later on it stagnated there while flowering in Greece and Rome. Northern Europe remained backward until the industrial revolution initiated the burst of creativity which leads white Europeans and Americans to claim superiority today. Sub-Saharan Africa, the absence of great civilizations in which is commonly cited as proof of Negro inferiority, is comparable to portions of the Western hemisphere. The South American Indians who occupied environments similar to those of Africa contributed very little to culture, while members of the same race who occupied Meso-America and the Andes created one of the great preindustrial civilizations.

As for race mixture, we need only recall that the "Rehoboth" of South Africa, a 19th century cross of Dutch and Hottentot, was more vigorous, taller and more fertile than either ancestor. Outstanding persons of mixed race today may owe their ability as much to their Negro as to their white ancestors. Individual ability, however, should not be confused with racial endowment. There is no evidence that races differ with respect to intelligence or aptitudes.

The overwhelmingly important need today is to maximize such abilities as all men possess; for culture is changing infinitely faster than we could breed superior men even if we knew how. At present, our scientific understanding of the physical world far exceeds our understanding of ourselves. The social and behavioral sciences are comparatively young, though they are beginning to mature. In fact, it is a striking feature of cultural evolution today that self-analysis—a probing of the cultural patterns that determine behavior—is not only permitted but encouraged. Instead of passing judgment according to traditional moral standards, science and religion (especially within the ecumenical movement) alike attempt to understand evolving behavior patterns and value systems.

Where Biology Leaves Off

3. *Is man's relationship to his world now primarily a cultural relationship?* Culture is, of course, limited by human capabilities and must meet basic biological needs; but, because these capabilities and needs are the same in all races, societies and environments, they are constants. Culture itself has evolved many goals that lie outside biological needs, and environments have conditioned cultures in various ways.

4. *Does anthropology now exist as the discipline that takes up evolutionary theory where biology leaves off?* Anthropology supplants biological theory with cultural theory appropriate to its data. Owing to recent cross-disciplinary research, other social sciences are expanding their scope from the present rather ethnocentric focus on our own culture to an approach to causality in cross-cultural dimension.

5. *What are the implications of evolutionary theory for the ways in which we understand and manage our social existence?* We must achieve deeper understanding of

how our societies evolved, how they function today and what factors are now transforming them at such unprecedented speed; and in all this we must avoid spurious biological analogies and racism. Although such understanding may, of course, be misused, few will doubt that the most benevolently motivated programs in both domestic and foreign affairs are handicapped by vast ignorance of crucial matters.

Processes of Cultural Evolution

The nature of cultural evolution is best exemplified in the substantive terms of particular factors and processes that have recently been postulated with some certainty. But, because the method is now empirical, it is not yet possible to offer universal principles or explanations. Hence all the generalizations that follow are subject to modification in proportion to their breadth.

Food hunters and collectors. The effect of the earliest cultural creations is best seen by consideration of the apes—baboons, chimpanzees and gorillas—that are most similar to our prehuman ancestors. The apes are terrestrial quadrupeds that travel within areas of only a half-dozen square miles, subsist almost entirely on vegetable foods and live in troops of from 20 to 50 individuals. In short, their societies represent ecological adaptations by animals with considerable adaptability but with no capacity for perpetuating learned behavior.

Owing to their bipedalism the first australopithecines could range much farther than the apes; they probably used cultural devices in collecting and, possibly, in transporting vegetable foods; and they ate meat—although how they obtained it without hunting paraphernalia is a mystery. Like the apes, these early hominids were limited to zones of mild climate where food was perennially available.

The cultural contrasts between the australopithecines and *Homo sapiens* were profound. The latter had means of hunting large and small game, processing and storing food, fishing, using fire, making clothing and, in some areas, supplementing human carriers with watercraft and sleds. Their societies adapted rather closely to the resources, climate and other factors of the environment, but there is evidence of supernaturalism connected with survival activities and death.

One important consequence of the invention of hunting skills was probably the evolution of the nuclear family—the basic unit of mother, father and immature children—which gave males an important and distinctive role that complemented the female role of food collecting and child tending. Prior to this, the family, consisting of the woman and her children, may have been matrifocal. It has recently been discovered that, among certain underprivileged segments of society where men have no important function in the family, the basic social unit is again being reduced to the matrifocal family. The nuclear family was certainly established by the Upper Palaeolithic period, which was a time of extensive hunting. Subsequently, the composition of small groups has been characterized by kinship relations that extend out from the nuclear family.

The nature of the hunting and gathering societies which have survived into recent times is clearly determined by cultural ecological adaptations, for all such societies possess the basic subsistence techniques. In areas of sparse resources, the primary subsistence band or unit is usually an aggregate of about 25 persons, but these bands intermarry with and relate in other ways to other bands within a maximum unit of not more than 500 persons. There is no strict territoriality, no defense of resources, no interband warfare. The popular belief that primitive tribes are constantly at war with one another—a belief that Robert Ardrey recently exploited in two articles in *Life* in order to represent defense of territory as a basic instinct in man and the root of all war—is simply without basis in fact. Hostilities between hunting and gathering bands were almost entirely limited to reprisals for death allegedly caused by witchcraft.

Special cultural and environmental factors caused certain variations among these simple bands. In the far north, dog sleds or toboggans and canoes enabled people to traverse much greater distances than could people who lived away from water or in warm climates and had to carry both equipment and babies on their backs. In some areas, such as the northwest coast of North America, the abundant fisheries supported large permanent villages which were able to develop a complicated social structure and a rich ceremonialism that would have been impossible among the small nomadic bands. In this case cultural ecological factors permitted latitude for considerable variation in the cultural superstructure.

Communities and states. Over the course of more than a million years, man evolved the biological potentials and the basic cultural factors that introduced variety among societies of food hunters and gatherers. Less than 10,000 years ago, his domestication of plants and animals permitted man to live in large permanent villages (not unlike those of the northwest coast fishers). A few thousand years later stratified state societies evolved. The emergence of supra-kin community institutions and of supra-community state institutions is the basis of an important methodological concept which happens to have a biological analogy (but does not on that account cast all cultural evolution in a biological framework).

We know that unicellular life was followed by multicellular forms (such as the jellyfish) wherein individual cells became specialized, dependent parts of the whole; that such forms evolved into more complex organisms in which cell clusters or organs acquired specialized functions within the whole animal. But this knowledge is based on inference from the past. The nature of the larger organism could not possibly have been deduced purely from an understanding of the earliest single-cell forms of life, no matter how complete this understanding, because the evolution of intercellular dependency resulted from particular and unforeseeable mutations that were possible only under special conditions. This does not mean that causality is negated. It signifies simply that the billions of species are understandable only in retrospect and that the successive higher levels of integration have qualities not contained in simpler levels.

There is a comparable succession of higher levels of sociocultural integration in cultural evolution, although there are also many substantively different lines of evolution. This cannot properly be considered an orthogenetic principle, for the nature of these levels of organization is no more fixed in culture than in biology. The earliest hominid bands were probably aggregates of matrifocal families; later bands consisted of nuclear families. Owing to the great variety of the forms of cultural ecological adaptations to the different environments, the kinship structure of these bands differed. Permanent communities also took different forms, but they tended to be similar where cultural and environmental factors were similar.

Meso-America and Mesopotamia

Early and Intermediate states. The earliest states—Egypt, Mesopotamia, the Indus valley, China, Meso-America and the central Andes—amalgamated the hitherto independent, egalitarian farm villages in similar although perhaps not identical ways. Local specialization and interdependency led at first to theocratic states, which later became militaristic. Surplus farm production released segments of the population to become special artisans, who created the beginnings of writing, mathematics, astronomy, architecture, metallurgy and other skills. Robert McC. Adams' *Evolution of Urban Society* (1966) has shown that the evolutionary processes were nearly identical in Meso-American and Mesopotamia despite outward differences in architectural forms, art styles and conceptualizations with regard to supernatural beings. Only empirical comparisons will show whether the other early states truly conformed to Adams' evolutionary model.

The spread of the ingredients of civilization led to establishment of new centers of innovation and state development, as in Greece, Rome, southeast Asia and Japan. Although these states represent a number of lines of evolutionary development, certain basic processes seem to have operated in most of them. Militarism had spread until waves of conquest that founded new dynasties characterized most areas after about 3,000 B.C. In time, strongly centralized controls and the oppression of the masses were undoubtedly a precondition of the appearance of great religious messiahs between about 600 B.C. and 600 A.D. The religions these messiahs founded were apparently a partial compensation for or escape from the misery that was the fate of the common man.

Technology's Far-Reaching Effects

The Industrial Revolution. The industrial revolution introduced wholly new kinds of factors. The application of science to production and the trade in manufactured commodities began with an era of mercantilism and led to an era of industrialization that has not yet reached its culmination (unless we say that automation and centralization represent new processes).

In northern Europe and North America, the social effect of the industrial revolution was to bring about the development of a commercial and manufacturing class that disrupted the traditional two-class, feudal-agrarian societies. Technology is now accelerating so rapidly that an individual often has to learn new skills several times during his life. Hence education has been given unprecedented importance. New employment skills have created an upward economic mobility which has facilitated upward social mobility. Evolution is now so rapid that change itself is becoming a goal. Whereas sociocultural systems and values formerly persisted for centuries or even millenniums, one now has to ask how briefly a social system, art form or other component of culture can endure and still be an integral part of the culture.

The processes and far-reaching effects of industrialization are by no means unique to the Western world. In the communist bloc, the trend is unmistakably toward a salaried population, whose advancement depends on education, which in turn inevitably broadens their outlook and weakens old ideologies. In the United States, the ideal of free enterprise is having to accommodate to the loss of family businesses, the increase in salaried positions in huge corporate enterprises and the decrease in the number of family farms. The principal difference between present trends in East and West seems to be that in the former the individual works for state-*owned* institutions while in the latter he works for what are coming to be state-*controlled* institutions. It seems safe to predict that though these processes are only incipient in China today, they will be manifest in the fully industrialized China of the future.

Few parts of the world have escaped completely the impact of the industrialized world. I recently directed a cross-cultural study of modernization among traditional populations in Africa, Asia and America which showed that these societies, whether originally independent tribes or members of states, have been drawn into the context of a cash economy. The people are aware of what money can buy, and they seek cash through their own production or through wage labor. Emergence of the goals of economic improvement and social mobility marked the end not only of colonial rule but of traditional tribal and state institutions. The manipulation of sources of wealth for individual benefit is destroying cultural heritages rooted in centuries of evolution.

Retrospect and Prospect

During many hundreds of thousands of years, cultural evolution proceeded slowly as man worked out his full biological potential and a cultural equipment that allowed him to develop different societies of food hunters and gatherers. The factors that explain these societies are limited in number and not difficult to understand; basically, each society had to adapt to the exigencies of its environment.

The so-called "agricultural revolution" introduced important new factors. Specialized production, economic interdependency, theocratic control of multicommunity states and social stratification were effects of the new factors or processes. Militarism and conquest for land or tribute were additional factors. For several millenniums, strongly class-structured states were perpetuated by military controls and sanctioned by state religions.

The industrial revolution introduced factors that disrupted the traditional two-class societies. The ensuing transformations were at first resisted by an appeal to long-established values and beliefs, but the point has now been reached when change is not only accepted but is becoming a goal for its own sake. But change seems to be getting out of hand. Every individual and every nation confront conflicting choices and expectations, and there are no clear guidelines for behavior.

To achieve some kind of stabilization and sense of direction, deeper understanding of the nature of change is needed. Already some insight into the nature of social conflicts, disjunctions, inequalities and confused goals has been gained. But scientific analysis cannot provide criteria by which to assess what is good, even though it may point to causal factors. In any society, starvation, physical suffering, a short life span and psychological disturbance are considered evils, but this fact gives no clue to whether societies not so afflicted will consider any of the possible alternatives good.

To avoid concluding on a gloomy note, however, I shall add that I am confident that an understanding of cultural evolution can make one fundamental contribution to human well-being. If we can identify the factors of change that originate in the industrial world and determine their probable effects (and I believe we can), it may be possible at least to mitigate some of the attending disruption. During many years of observing efforts to direct change among preliterate societies, it has become clear to me that success consists less in determining the general direction of change than in understanding it sufficiently well to prevent the many traumatic effects it so often entails.

EVOLUTIONARY SCIENCE AND THE DILEMMA OF FREEDOM AND DETERMINISM

Our control over ourselves and our destiny seems in no wise to be more within our grasp since the rise of science than before.

LANGDON GILKEY

The sciences of man raise many issues for philosophical and theological reflection. In this article we shall limit ourselves to the most hoary but probably most significant issue of all: freedom and determinism, and their complex interrelations in a scientific age. For it is precisely at this point that the difficulties and, even more, the relevance of theological discourse about man appear today.

At the outset it is important to note that the question of the relation of freedom and determinism is not, as is sometimes supposed, an issue raised only by the religious community over against the scientific community, the former standing for "free will" and the latter for "determinism." On the contrary, it is an issue invariably posed *within* scientific thought about man. It appears, with all its familiar paradoxical and baffling force, in scientific writings about man even if no religious questions, categories or aims are mentioned. Let us, then, look first at what recent scientific views of man have implied with regard to determinism and human freedom, and see how in this new context the old puzzle reappears, unbidden and unexpected but very much there. For the evolutionary sciences speak about man with two

Dr. Gilkey is professor of theology at the University of Chicago divinity school.

quite different voices, and as a result the lay reader of these studies is likely to experience as much confusion as clarification when he asks in their light, "What sort of being am I? Am I determined or am I in some sense free?"

Certainly, the first impact of the evolutionary sciences on the understanding of man has been to increase immeasurably the sense that man is determined in all he does. According to the Darwinian hypothesis, man in his total nature arose out of preceding material and organic factors by the processes of purely natural causation; that is, through the interactions of random mutations and natural selection. In this sense man is for evolutionary thought "just an animal" whose origin can be spelled out exhaustively in terms of his natural and animal background.

Blind Mutations and Natural Selection

While subsequent evolutionary theory, especially in the field of genetics, has modified this hypothesis, it has not in any sense changed it with regard to our problem. The fundamental character of the explanations offered for man—as produced by blind mutations and natural selection—has not altered; consequently there has been no tendency on the part of these sciences to retract or soften the basic view that man is to be understood as a product of the determined life of nature. (See, for instance, the two preceding articles in this series.) Needless to say, the more recent developments of the psychological and social sciences—explaining man's consciousness, learning processes, categories of thought, values, goals and behavior patterns, in terms of various determining psychological and social forces—have added to this picture of man as, from top to bottom, an *effect* of nonrational determinants rather than the intentional ini-

tiator or *cause* of events. And the development of an
"electronic" understanding of man has only seemed to
cap this process. A computer can apparently do almost
all we can do; and if that is so, there seems to many to
be nothing left for "freedom" or "spirit" to do, just as—
with a chemically and biologically explained life, a van-
ished soul, and the computerized mind—there seems to
be no "place" in man's makeup where freedom might
reside. Scientific conclusions about man seem to spell
out one continuous message: man is a determined creature through and through, a result of invariant causal
interrelations, a factor within a necessitating natural
process; and consequently in the scientific account of
man there is no longer any evidence of or any room for
the traditional category of freedom. Apparently, say
many, the old problem of "free will" has disappeared
in our age, for science can find no such entity when it
inquires into the nature of man.

Science as Champion of Freedom

There is, however, another voice with which the sciences of man speak about man, and this voice seems to
be giving us precisely the opposite message about ourselves. For in a slightly different context, the same scientists tell us roughly the following: the new knowledge
about man through evolutionary biology, genetics and
cultural anthropology can, if we are able only to will so
to use it and to make the right decisions, lead to man's
control over his own destiny. Heretofore, evolution has
been blind and its results have been contingent and un-
planned, the outcome of no purpose or mind, divine or
human; now, however, with human knowledge and its
resultant possibilities for control over these determining
factors, man himself and society, and so the course of
evolution and history, are coming under human control

and guidance. Thus we are faced at present with crucial possibilities that challenge our moral sense and our rationality, and that call for mature and responsible decisions from all of us. Shall we use this knowledge creatively to form a more rational, more secure, more peaceful and more democratic life for all, or shall we use it to destroy ourselves?

At the conclusion of most articles and books on man as understood by the new sciences, the issue of the responsible and creative *use* of our knowledge is pointedly raised over and over, in language which we can only call the traditional language of "freedom." It includes such key words as "responsible," "rational," "moral," "choice," "decisions," "purposes," and thus seems to paint a quite different picture of man than did the other voice. *As scientific and technological man,* man is here seen as an initiating moral and rational cause as well as a determined effect of natural and historical forces—which is what the category of "freedom" has traditionally sought all along to say. To the cynical observer it might almost seem that the category of freedom, if defended by theologians or philosophical idealists, is inadmissible in a scientific age, but that the same category, voiced by the scientific community, is thoroughly in tune with the aims and aspirations of that community.

Ironically, therefore, in this new context created by the possibilities of the use of scientific knowledge, science appears not at all as the destroyer of freedom, but as its most robust champion. For whatever we may mean by that strange word, we do at least mean a sense of control over the determining fates through intentional activity; that is, rational activity directed at chosen ends. And by "fates" we mean the blind forces of nature, of genetic inheritance, of disease and uncontrolled scarcity, of social structure and tradition, of local or family custom and, most important, of the inner psyche—all those forces that shape human existence in directions antithetical to or destructive of conscious human goals and purposes.

Through scientific knowledge and through its resultant technology, man has come to feel, in a way never experienced before, that he can, through actions based on that knowledge, control these forces toward his own ends; man feels "freer" than ever before to shape his *own* destiny. Such feeling is reflected in almost every book about modern science and its effects on our life. Thus we say that science in our day has vastly increased in the scientist himself an awareness of freedom—though, as noted, his *conclusions* about man as a totally determined being tend to point in just the opposite direction. Very rarely are these two views of man brought together in any sort of conceptual unity; rather, they appear usually in different parts of a book or an article, the determined image dominating the section concerned with "what we know about man," and the free image taking over when the future uses of scientific knowledge are discussed.

Inherent Paradox

How are we to understand this paradox, if not self-contradiction, of determinism and freedom in scientific discourse about man—a paradox familiar enough in the history of philosophy and theology but surprising amid the precisions of scientific language? The paradox, let us suggest, is inherent in the function or role of science in our culture. For science appears, so to speak, in two somewhat different roles: first, as a body of hypotheses or conclusions about the nature and interrelation of things, including man; second, as a means through which scientific man creatively knows his world and thereby exercises a new-found control over his world, including his own species. Inevitably, the first of these "roles" moves in the direction of determinism, the latter toward a sense of freedom.

In the first case we are thinking of science as a series of hypotheses, a body of conclusions, about the nature, functioning and interrelations of the various objects of its inquiries. In this instance we are asking: "What does science say about man: what do we know through science of our own nature, our origins, our capacities?" Scientific answers to these questions always present to us a picture of a determined creature whose rise, organism, functions and powers are exhaustively explained in the terms of the causal nexus. This picture of a determined being is presented for two reasons: First (as Professor Steward stated in the preceding chapter), scientific inquiry necessarily proceeds "*as if* natural laws operate without exception—*as if* . . . all aspects of human behavior had determinants." A scientific explanation subsists as an explanation in terms of such determinants. For a number of reasons, science as a mode of inquiry is committed to finding and elaborating the invariable relations or "causes" that bring its object of inquiry into being and so explain it. To invoke a factor outside this causal nexus is, therefore, to leave the realm of scientific explanation. Consequently, whatever object science seeks to explain must be explained in terms of its necessitating, causal interrelationships; that is what scientific inquiry says about man and that is all it can say about him.

Second, the object of scientific inquiry is always just that: an *object*, manipulated and passive; that is, it is understood with regard to the observable and measurable forces that impinge upon it and work within it; it is spoken about insofar as it is determined. Thus its *subject* character, as self-caused or self-determining, tends to disappear under scientific scrutiny; or else it reappears only in statistical tables, where it is at best only implicit or totally random. As an object of scientific inquiry, then, man is from the outset, by the nature of the method of scientific cognition, understood as a determined being. This is a valid aspect of man, and so vastly informative. Whether it provides an exhaustive "explanation" of man, or whether, if taken alone, it leads to a creative understanding of man, is another question—one that scientific inquiry cannot settle by itself, since its answer is already predetermined for it by what it regards as a valid explanation and so a valid understanding. In any case, we can understand why a goodly number of contemporary philosophers, especially existentialists and phenomenologists, have challenged the naturalistic and positivistic thesis that the only forms of valid knowledge about human existence are provided by the scientific method.

When, however, we think of science not as a body of knowledge but as a creative enterprise on the part of the scientific community, through which it can use that knowledge for human purposes, an entirely different picture of man, his nature and capacities is implied. In this context, as we saw, the scientist's sense of his own freedom, of his intentional—i.e., rational and purposive—control over himself and his destiny is vastly enhanced. The reason for his sudden change of mood with regard to freedom is that the scientist's focus of intention has shifted: his gaze is no longer on another man as the *object* of scientific inquiry, but now on himself as the *inquirer*, as the knower of objects through active manipulation and by means of that knowledge the potential controller of other objects and even of himself. He has ceased to look at the "specimen" in the laboratory or the patient on the bed; he is now gazing at himself, the man in the white coat. In the one case man appears as a small, passive, determined object in the blind flux of events; in the other he expands into a wise, powerful, active, and so free subject directing that flux through his knowledge according to his own purposes.

In the latter case the *knower* of science, as the rational and purposive manipulator of his environment, correctly feels in himself all those capacities of intentionality and freedom which the most extreme idealistic or religious philosophies in history have ever granted to man. In other words, here is the explanation of the paradox latent in scientific writings about man: in the part of his publication where man appears as determined, the author is writing about man as the object he studies; in the part where man appears as free, he is writing about his own community of scientists and so about man as he is himself aware of man; i.e., as a rational and purposive subject.

The Secular Mood

In sum, modern culture, dominated in many of its images of man by science, produces two very diverse pictures of man, one determined and one free, one that of a creature of the flux and the other that of the creative manipulator of it. These two almost contradictory images involve, in terms of the interests and capacities of a scientific culture, many of the same puzzles of determinism and freedom that baffled the theologians of an earlier culture oriented to religious issues. If there ever was a paradox in the self-understanding of man, this one, created by science, certainly is it!

Traditional theological reflection has generated its own forms of the determinism-freedom paradox, centering largely on the questions of God's providence and his grace and their respective relation to human freedom. These are, for the theologian, real and significant contemporary as well as historical issues. Our concern here, however, is with the question: What are the theological implications of this twofold image of man, as a determined creature and as a free lord, which the enterprise of science has presented to our age?

We should, I believe, recognize that this paradoxical picture has been an important factor in the genesis of the "secular mood" of our time. "Secularism" is a viewpoint, characteristic of our urban culture, which sees external reality as determined by blind, contingent forces —and so devoid of any traces of the divine. On the other hand, the same viewpoint sees man as "come of age," as a mature, responsible, rational and moral creature who through his scientific, technological and industrial powers can solve all his major problems—and so is in no "need" of a God even if there were one. Because the scientific enterprise inevitably fosters the view that the *objects* of inquiry, the known, are determined beings, while the *subjects* of inquiry, the knowers, are rational, moral and so free beings, science has been largely instrumental in the creation of this paradoxical secular mood; and correspondingly, any problems or contradictions in these two images produced by science will be reproduced in the naturalistic secularism which is its cultural and philosophical expression. In any case, it is evident how much the current radical theologies, which declare that God is dead in our time and that man has "come of age" as his own problem-solver, depend on the view of man and his world created by the scientific enterprise.

What Theology Says

But what does theological reflection have to say about this twofold view of man? It has two demurrals which could be summed up in the reminder to the scientific community that the "man" whom they study as the determined object of knowledge is the same creature whom as knower and manipulator they recognize as a free and rational being. Thus, for the theologian, man is *less* determined than science, understood as a body of knowledge, seems to indicate, and *more* determined than the possibility of its own creative use of that knowledge apparently implies to the scientific community.

The methods of science must be qualified when science speaks of what it "knows" about man. For the scientist as knower does not regard his *own* knowing or his own use of that knowledge as determined; and he surely reacts vigorously (as the A.M.A. illustrates) if he feels that *he*, as a scientist or a physician, is about to be manipulated or controlled by the forces of government or of economic power. If, then, he is to be consistent, his apprehension of himself as a free person who knows and acts on the basis of his knowledge should be read back into his objective knowledge of other men as determined, lest on the intellectual level he be betrayed into the paradox we have outlined.

More important, it is necessary that the scientist understand the freedom of even the "object" man, lest he find himself manipulating other men as mere objects. The hope of the scientist for the future of mankind depends, as we have seen, largely on his confidence that through knowledge he can manipulate man for "human purposes" much as he has controlled natural objects and other forms of animal life. Such control of man on a society-wide scale could be very dangerous indeed unless the scientist realized deeply that the men he seeks to control are not like the inanimate objects of engineering, but rather are as much characterized by personal freedom and rationality as is he, the knower. One of the most significant things the humanities, and among them theology, can do is to keep reminding the scientific elite that when the latter suggest schemes for the control of "man," it is fellow citizens and not objects with which these schemes propose to deal; and that because this is so, the control of man's destiny through scientific knowledge is fraught with the political dangers of tyranny and the social dangers of dehumanization. A *strictly* scientific view of man might tend to regard society as a vast laboratory in which only the scientific manipulator and his political bosses retain their freedom. The sciences of man can greatly forward the human enterprise, but only if the purposive knowers who control application of the sciences are willing to grant to man as the object of knowledge and control the same freedom and personal identity they presuppose in themselves.

Theological reflection can also point out that there is *less* freedom in the knower and controller through his knowledge than most descriptions of the potential uses of science seem to assume. It is strange but true that in *this* context theology stresses the determination of man, while science emphasizes his absolute and unconditioned freedom. Our suggestion, in other words, is that some of that sense of the determination of man's reason and will by forces outside and within himself, which is taken for granted in scientific accounts about man as an object, should be read back into our thought about scientific man as subject, as knower and doer.

Knowledge as Power

Knowledge is power; it results almost invariably in the power to control that which is now known. Correspondingly, knowledge about man can lead potentially to the power to control other men and hence human destiny. But new power, even power through knowledge, by no means guarantees the virtue of the controller. In engineering, technology or medicine the use of scientific knowledge seldom directly involves any serious moral temptations for the scientist. His power in the laboratory and over wider natural forces is not the kind that corrupts. Guided morally by the noble standards of his profession, he is aware only of his freedom to enact his largely benevolent purposes on an uncomplaining nature. Thus he is inclined to think that even when he uses this knowledge to control men rather than nature, his power to control will retain the "academic" benevolence of the laboratory, and so remain uncorrupted.

When men exert *social* power over other men, they have left behind the laboratory, the engineering camp or the hospital and have entered the murky and ambiguous realm of politics. Our only valid experimental evidence about how men use power in society is given by political and economic history, not by scientific experiments in the laboratory. And history is grimly unequivocal on one point: that power universally corrupts its users. That is to say, the men who control others in the political arena are not as free to control *themselves* by reason and moral will as they themselves assume or as are the men in a laboratory. Men in politics are in fact determined by forces of ambition and self-interest and of anxiety about their class, nation or race—forces which twist the rationality of their minds and the morality of their wills and so seriously diminish their control over what they do. Somehow in history rational plans and good intentions are seldom realized. The recent great increase in man's ability to control others through technology has not led to any corresponding increase in his self-control. Rather, in the political arena an increment of power tends to increase a man's bondage to his own self-concern.

Inner Bondage

The empirical evidence, through history, of this inner bondage is overwhelming: power does corrupt. The scientist authors who speak so hopefully of a "new day" for man through the power of scientific knowledge are well aware of history's evidence. Yet they express unbounded confidence in the almost total freedom of scientific man to act rationally and morally with his knowledge. Apparently they feel that scientific knowledge somehow tempers the self-interest of the inquirer, and shuts off in him the power of the many forces that generally determine human action in irrational directions. Here, therefore, we can speak only of "faith," the faith that the determining forces scientific minds see acting on others will not subvert *their* freedom when that freedom is guided by a sufficient scientific understanding.

Every class in the world's history has assumed a similarly fond view of its own virtues: monarchs, philosophers, priests and presbyters (the worst of all), merchants and so on. And history has shown each such vision to be a self-delusion. The Greeks too, as is well known, believed that the kind of knowledge they valued led to virtue and freedom—but for them "knowledge" meant wisdom and not *techne,* knowledge directed at *self-*control rather than at the control of what is external to the self. Modern scientific knowledge, on the other hand, being directed entirely at objects outside the self, implies no such deep transformation of the inner self with its freedom to do evil, and yet it is taken to be in some sense the new grace that will soften men's hearts.

This is, perhaps, the most important demurral that theology (or history) might bring to the sciences of man. Man as a whole is more free than scientific knowledge declares him to be, but scientific man is more determined—by the social forces of class, nation and race, and the inward forces of hostility, anxiety and ambition —than many of those who propose social uses of scientific knowledge seem to admit. Only if a scientific society realizes how ambiguously its potent knowledge and techniques can be used can it deal creatively with the new political and ethical problems which these new powers raise.

Myths to Be Reassessed

As we are continually reminded, since the 17th century science has taken away from the traditional religious community its earlier (and to us childish) faith that man stood at the center of a world created for his sole benefit and salvation. In our day a wise theology will question the peculiar faith of much of the scientific community in the power of scientific man benevolently to determine the destiny of the race. In both these cases new problems with regard to the meaning of the human story are posed for us by the loss of a rather naive faith. For in *both* it is the myth by which a cultural community expresses its hopes that has been critically questioned. Today, as throughout history, mankind lives in terms of "myths"—the "religious" myth that man has been set in the center of things by a sovereign divine will, or the "scientific" myth that scientific man can sovereignly determine his own destiny and freely alter the march of historical events to suit his chosen moral purposes. Today, as in the past, intelligence requires that we ponder critically the empirical validity of these myths.

A scientific age, which has added immensely to our understanding and so to our powers, has not made us more virtuous; nor has it made the meanings of our life any more secure. Our control over ourselves and our destiny seems in no wise to be more within our grasp than before. The old theological problems of the use man makes of his freedom, of his bondage to self-interest, and of the ultimate meaning of the human story, have not been dissolved but rather have been increased by the sciences of man. And in a scientific age, which has added to our knowledge if not to our self-understanding, intelligent and realistic convictions about ourselves and our place in the scheme of things are more necessary than ever.

MAN, CULTURE, EVOLUTION AND ENVIRONMENT

Philosophers and theologians must become cognizant of the varied interpretations of scientific findings and judge them without bias.

JOHN R. JABLONSKI

For thousands of years science, the creation of man, has been affecting man and his society. As man evolved from his primitive state, his awareness of the world around him increased. Presently he learned to record his observations and so laid the foundations of science. As he began to organize this recorded information he saw that it had both practical and philosophical applications. His data on the movement of the stars, for example, probably led to telling time and inventing numbers, thus to a system of counting which was the origin of mathematics. As man continued his observations and noted the constancy of things and the regularity of movements in nature, and as he developed technical skills, he arrived at a disciplined understanding of matter—i.e., physics and chemistry. Soon he saw how these three branches of knowledge—mathematics, physics and chemistry—were interrelated. Much later when the organic phase of chemistry synthesized its first molecule, another branch of science came into being: modern biology. Meanwhile, man's attempt to understand his own nature had led to the discipline of psychology, whose major object today is to explain the individual's relationship to himself and to his environment.

Dr. Jablonski is professor of biology at Boston University.

Adaptive Survival

All these categorizations and organizations of knowledge presumably took place after man became a societal animal, and approximately during the same period of human history. Sociology, however, could develop only after all these other disciplines had taken shape, for it depended on these for the comprehensive analysis on which alone prediction can be based. The total of all these disciplines has become embodied in what we call "culture," each culture having as many dimensions as there are developed disciplines operating in it.

Throughout history, as all these fields of knowledge evolved, philosophy or theology has attempted to provide a unifying principle. In an isolated society, where one or other of these disciplines—or all of them—is lacking, philosophy and theology remain simple as befits that society's needs. But where, as in modern Western society, most or all of these disciplines are implemented to a tremendous degree, philosophy and theology are infinitely complex and involved.

This is the story of man's growth in knowledge as I see it. It is a story of change begetting change begetting change. These disciplines themselves tend to change in order to explain more adequately the ever larger total revealed through continuing investigation conducted by rational and inquisitive man. Thus I see evolution at work not only in the formal sciences but also in cultural and philosophical thought and expression. For science and philosophy have a common aim: to codify observations into a system of "laws" that will enable man to predict the outcome of his undertakings.

Thus man can be seen as a result of evolution—of natural selection and what I prefer to call "adaptive survival." And not only man, but all his cultures have shown the signs of adaptive survival, can be said to be evolving along with evolving man. To put it another way: since man makes the culture, it must evolve as he does, and change occurs as a result of and not just for the sake of change. Where evolving man is involved, there is change.

In an earlier article in this book Langdon Gilkey presented a picture of man as paradoxically both determined and free—determined by external forces and at the same time endowed with freedom of choice. Hence man's dilemma: how shall he handle the scientific achievements that have the potential to alter drastically the environment in which the individual's inherited characteristics find expression?

Controlled Breeding

To deal with this question we must examine a number of views lately put forth by men of science. Most important is the statement that human breeding can be controlled in whatever direction is decided on. The fact is, of course, that sufficient evidence is on hand to show that man-controlled breeding works when other animals or plants are the subjects, but not when man makes himself the subject. This peculiarity appears to be related to the human ego and to inner conflict, neither of which lends itself to investigation. Moreover, controlled production of the human species is at present inseparable from value judgments. Thus when Western science warns the nations with large populations and small food resources that they are producing too many people, they become resentful, for they see the West enjoying an overabundance of food and other goods. Nor is it true, as some scientists pretend, that survival and reproduction are a totally random process in our species. There results in the evolutionary process an imbalance in favor of the segment of society that can supply the needs of its individuals. Here again the environment plays an important role, since it is the most variable and potentially the most controllable factor in the picture.

Again, generally speaking, it is the well adapted individuals who leave progeny. But modern medicine enables many otherwise "unfit" individuals to survive to the age at which they can reproduce. Thus a gene pool that may not be adapted for survival is preserved. Another consideration is that since major evolutionary changes are produced by the slow shift in individual biological adaptability, imposition on a population (with or without its consent) of modern scientific techniques of birth control can bring about unimaginable changes in the species—changes that may or may not be desirable. Also, when selection is effected in a natural or artificial breeding population, some inherited characteristics become more prominent than others and tend to overshadow the organism's whole potential. That this is so appears in precise genetic studies of individuals. Characteristics that are masked by the predominant characteristics are never identified and may continue unrecognized until special selection or chance response to environmental changes brings them into the open. Finally, we must be reminded that the rate of change is probably the most important feature of evolution. Today science can use mathematical models to determine rates and predict expected and unexpected changes. But scientific man can apply only the facts he knows and understands. He is far from knowing *all* the facts.

Living Beings by Synthesis?

In the course of his evolution, man has instituted tremendous alterations in the environment and thus made room for new expressions in his own species. The process has been circular, so to speak. Each alteration has af-

fected its instigator, his society and culture and ultimately his philosophy, all of which in turn produced further alteration. In theory, man constantly probes the
fundamental structure, nature, in quest of "Truth." No
limits are placed on such an endeavor, and probably none
should be. But the application of the findings is something else. Today science is on the point of synthesizing
macro-molecules (the larger and more complex molecules most commonly found in living systems). In a
recent telecast called "The 21st Century," one of my fellow biologists made it clear that he feels this event is imminent. He and his colleagues are talking about the
arrangement of the molecules to form human life, as if
this were just a matter of scientific course. I have used
the word "form" rather than "create" human life, because
I am persuaded that life is not only and merely a bi-
ologic sequence. When and if the synthesis of a living
being occurs, it will be too late for the humanists and
theologians to try to arrive at an understanding of what
is "human" and what "animal."

However, as a teaching and research scientist I am
obliged to look more critically at this idea. The popular
understanding is that science will discover the secret of
life. But the popular understanding may well be a mis-
understanding. For instance, Barry Commoner, writing
on "The Elusive Code of Life" in the *Saturday Review*
(October 1, 1966), contends that the road to complete
understanding of the Code of Life stretches into the re-
motest future, perhaps into a never-never land. Dr. Commoner is by no means the only biologist who holds this
opinion. Thus the dilemma in which society is caught—
not the conflict as to the possibility of synthesizing life in
a test tube, but the conflicting conclusions based on the
same scientific data. It is a dilemma for philosophical and
theological scholars to deal with. They must become
aware of the varied interpretations of scientific findings
and judge them without bias.

Altering Ovulation

Moving back to the area of controlled breeding, we note that the use of certain hormones to alter ovulation is now commonplace in Western society. As yet statistics on the number of users, their theological inclinations and their reasons for using these hormones are far from accurate, but it is obvious that this single discovery has had a social impact that is still developing. Just what kind of Pandora's box this is will require much more time and observation to discover. As yet it is impossible to predict how the environment will be modified. In other words, sound evaluation of this hormone discovery requires *time* above all. Remember another recent pharmacological discovery—the tranquilizer pill that could be consumed in large quantities without lethal effects to the user. Many pregnant women took this promising medication to relieve depression. The consequence was unalterable abnormalities in many of the young. What I am suggesting is not a ban on new drugs but more exhaustive preliminary experimentation and control, especially where the drug might be used by women of childbearing age. This caveat of course applies to "the pill."

It would seem then that the use made of discoveries is directed not only by the findings of scientific experimentation. The examples I have cited suggest that by and large the individual is less concerned to use his "freedom" to effect environmental improvements for all than to improve his own chances of survival. And this intense desire to improve his survival potential encourages man's scientific impatience; he is loath to allow sufficient time either for discussion of the proper application of new discoveries or for exhaustive testing.

In general, man does not attempt to interfere with scientific endeavor so long as science comes up with more successes than failures and so long as it is used to improve his world. In the final analysis, however, science must be assessed on philosophical rather than utilitarian grounds. Take, for example, the issues raised by the formation of tissue and organ banks as a means to aid survival. Today most surgical operations involving tissue and organ transplanting are successful. In the light of this development, two questions must be dealt with: (1) Does the necessary tampering with the individual's system constitute an alteration of his essential being? (2) In making it possible for such individuals to survive and reproduce, is society maintaining gene pools incapable of adequately adapting to environmental conditions? Scientific research has by no means yet determined whether biological alteration would be detrimental to the human species over a long period of time. But even if no such danger exists, philosophers and theologians should seek to determine if there is any limit to the amount of alteration possible before a person loses his identity. Their deliberations should also include consideration of the eugenically oriented sperm bank. The supposition that artificial insemination will produce superior offspring is highly dubious, since the process of independent assortment and random selection of genes can never be guaranteed. Although genetic determination is still a somewhat haphazard science, the development of the sperm bank constitutes a serious theological problem.

Dangers in Drugs

On the other side of the fertility coin is the development of new drugs: on the one hand to increase the potential for conception (these drugs have been most effective, giving rise to numbers of multiple births); and on the other to effect rejection of the fertilized egg in the wall of the uterus, thereby bringing about a chemical abortion. Theologians and scientists must scrutinize these and other developments in order to understand their scope, meaning and implication. Personally I feel that scientists should not by themselves determine the proper use of the drugs they have developed.

The attempt to understand the functions of the individual in his evolving world has been paralleled by an increasing emphasis on understanding how man makes decisions, feels, responds and develops his own identity. For example, groups such as that headed by F. O. Schmitt, professor at M.I.T. and chairman of the neurosciences research program, are exploring the functioning of the brain in an effort to comprehend fully its neural, psychological and molecular interactions. Already they have concluded that competent researchers will eventually be able to analyze the psyche and predict its characteristics. This kind of experimentation is of course vital, but I am not convinced that the knowledge gained will be used wisely; I find no evidence of the kind of controls that would be needed to dispense such knowledge properly.

The use of hallucinogenic drugs to "expand" the mind in an effort to improve perception is another example of man's ability to change his environment. Here again the problem is that of use of an agent without sufficient understanding of its physiological and psychological effects. Moreover, the various reasons given to justify use of such drugs—as an avenue to "mystical experience," etc.—testify to man's determination to experiment with his environment without proper scientific supervision. The widespread use of these drugs is an indictment of the scientific community for unleashing a compound prior to making a complete study, and an indication that although scientific control and legal enforcement are becoming increasingly difficult, inquisitive man is employing the time-tested empirical method without rational consideration of the probable results of his investigations.

Pollution and Productivity

Ultimately, the issue is one of freedom. Consider the problem of pollution and the environmental changes it brings about. Man is caught up in a vicious circle: modern life demands urban living, and urban living accelerates the process of pollution; the pollutants are the products of industrialization, which is the offspring of increased technological development. And apparently the situation is not going to improve: since industrial progress brings in its train cultural changes that directly affect modern man, any improvement is contingent on greater regulation of industry. But man, who too often equates increased happiness with increased productivity, insists that the commercial enterprise remain free of burdensome restriction. When this attitude is combined with the false notion that pollution is a political problem removed from the ordinary citizen's concern, man forfeits his decision-making role to government; cultural regression is the result.

There is a remote possibility that catastrophic changes in the environment—e.g., smog attacks—have an evolutionary effect. The fact that some people die as a consequence of such changes while others do not may be a dramatic illustration of the theory of the survival of the fittest. In any case, science and philosophy must come to some agreement as to how to approach the new problems that are the concomitants of scientific progress. For not only is man's existence in danger, but his cultural fabric is being torn asunder.

Finally, modern medical science is moving toward

early detection of disease. In some cases treatment of a disease can begin when the victim is very young, and any offspring that he produces may or may not carry the gene potential for the disease. Since observation of many generations will be required before the congenitalness of the disease can be assessed, it will be necessary to decide on moral grounds whether its treatment should entail prohibition of the individual from undertaking parenthood. Even now, however, we have some knowledge of the heritance patterns of certain diseases— knowledge which can be drawn on to advise a person whether to produce offspring or whether he and his spouse should adopt children to complete their family. Such genetic counseling could well mitigate against some of the pitfalls of natural evolution.

As modern man continues to search for longer life, sufficient food and full use of his potential, he will increasingly replace manual activity with computerized machines. Heretofore the psychological reaction against use of the computer has prevented its full exploitation. But in all probability so many devices will be developed that man will be forced to face the problem of how to use his leisure time wisely. In sum, man must continually assess his developments and discoveries in the light of their possible repercussions on society.

In speculating on how the evolution of man and his culture will affect him, I have tried to accentuate the high degree of disciplinary interrelationship. Since every significant change will affect many areas of life, we must appraise all of man's discoveries and actions carefully if future generations are to find the proper mixture of scientific advance and humanist thought to enable mankind to continue to evolve through the process of adaptive survival.

SHALL WE PLAY GOD?

Biological advances, accomplished and potential, compel us to decide now what direction manipulation is to take.

LEROY AUGENSTEIN

Charles Darwin not only initiated the theory of the evolution of man; he also initiated an evolution in man's thinking about himself. In bringing to the fore questions about how we got here he forced mankind to examine again the questions: What is man? Why is he here? Consequently he antagonized many people. Some saw no reason to question beliefs which had served them for a long time, others who were needlessly secure in their beliefs did not want to think, still others did not like the implied downgrading of man inherent in Darwin's theories. In particular, those theories seemed to imply a less personal and interfering God than many people desired.

New scientific developments are forcing us to examine again those age-old questions: What is man? Why are we here? This time, however, the impetus comes not from considerations of man's origins, but rather from the need to know where we should go from here. To put much of the new scientific knowledge to proper use will require that we carefully consider the further question: What would we like for man to be?

Since we are now capable of controlling man's very

Dr. Augenstein is chairman of the department of biophysics at Michigan State University, East Lansing, Michigan. Portions of this article are based on passages in his upcoming book, *Come Let Us Play God* (all rights reserved to the author).

essence, such considerations no longer reflect a downgrading of man, but rather a great elevation of man's
responsibility. As a consequence, we must continue that
evolution of man's reflection on his own role which
was initiated by Darwin. His theories raised questions
about just how intimately God has been involved "on a
day-to-day basis" in (1) the creation of man and (2)
the determination of how man was to evolve. Now, what
with the new developments in science, we must ask: To
what extent should man participate in determining his
final destiny? In other words, to what extent is man a
creature of God, and to what extent must he be a co-
partner with him in assuming responsibility for controlling the universe?

The kinds of scientific advances which are forcing us
to this re-evaluation are occurring in various areas. These
include such developments as our making "spare parts"
to allow people to live almost indefinitely, our seeking
to determine how the mind functions so that we will be
able to control "brainwashing," our acquiring the ability
to predict birth defects and to control man's hereditary
potential, our devising methods for reducing the death
rate (and thereby augmenting the population explosion).
Perhaps the best way to illustrate the challenge we face
is to look briefly at some of these new discoveries and
the dilemmas involved in putting them to use.

Mind Manipulation

One of the most exciting new areas of research lies
in exploration of the functioning of the mind. To a large
extent this is the real frontier in science today. But
though there is still much to learn in this area, already
we possess knowledge which not only makes possible
a measure of control over an individual's thoughts but

also gives some inkling as to the kind of manipulation which may be feasible later.

Early in the space race many people began to wonder what would happen if astronauts entered the isolation of space for perhaps months on end. One of the groups investigating this question is at work at McGill University in Montreal. Initially the researchers wanted to know what happens to an individual placed in isolation with no access to sensory information. They built an isolation room which was sound- and vibration-proof, with no drafts and with carefully controlled lights. Students were hired as subjects for the isolation-endurance tests; they could speak to persons outside the room through a microphone, but there was no way for outside sounds to enter. The students used all sorts of clever tricks to try to get those on the outside to communicate with them; one claimed that the toilet was overflowing and that unless someone came to his assistance immediately, he would drown.

Most of the students were neither so original nor so dishonest, but almost all of them tried to communicate with those outside the room. So the experimenters decided to find out what the students would accept as communication. They installed a switch so that each time a student flipped it he would hear a very long and obnoxious commercial. Amazingly, some students who stayed in the room as long as two days replayed the commercial as many as 50 times. To find out whether they were really listening or were just seeking to break the monotony, the researchers replaced the commercial with an equally long harangue claiming that flying saucers are real. This too was played over and over again. Although none of the students admitted to believing in flying saucers on first entering the room, when they came out they all not only professed belief in them but tried to convert their roommates to their belief. Thus it would seem that under sensory deprivation a person is willing to erase previously acquired information and write in new.

Clearly, the mind-manipulation technique can be used for good or for evil. Consider that 50 per cent of our hospital beds are occupied by mental patients. Suppose we developed this technique to such a degree that mental patients could be told: "Forget the old rules and regulations by which you have been operating; here is a new good set." That would be one of the finest gifts any scientist could give to society. By the same token we know what the Chinese communists have done with brainwashing.

Here is the dilemma: Information about how the brain works is neither good nor bad per se; the good and the bad come into play when someone decides what is bad which must be erased, what is good which must be written in. As I see it, it is at this point that ethical and moral implications enter. One cannot really determine "good" and "bad" unless he carefully considers our earlier questions: What is man? Why is he here?

Spare Parts Available

A second research area of great promise and importance is the making of spare parts to replace the vital organs of human beings. It may soon be possible to replace defective organs in one of two or three ways. One way is by developing synthetic (plastic or metal) parts which perform as well as healthy natural parts. Heart valves were the first such artificial organs to be developed; the plastic heart followed; eventually we may develop miniaturized versions of the present bulky heart-lung machine, the kidney machine and so on.

Another way of replacing organs is by transplanting them from one individual to another or even from one species to another. Though it is difficult not to be impressed by the complicated operations involving large teams of medical personnel and sophisticated equipment, this technique poses a number of problems. In particular, except where identical twins are involved, transplantations cause strong reactions in the recipient since his body treats the incoming cells as an invasion by foreign material. Therefore we must destroy by drugs or radiation the recipient's ability to produce antibodies, and since this makes it impossible for him to fight off bacterial infections, he must be loaded up with antibiotics. In fact, today more kidney recipients die from subsequent infections for which we have no effective antibiotic than from the actual operations involved in the transplant.

Techniques to change the external coats of the cells in the transplant organ may make it possible to "fool" the receiving body so that its immune response does not recognize the cells as "foreign." It is now possible to force human cells developed in test tubes to fuse and to exchange some of their genetic material; as a consequence the exterior of the cells is modified. But even if by some such means we are able to surmount some of the above-cited complications, we still face the problem of getting a large enough supply of organs for all who need them.

The solution will require taking cells from an individual's body and reconstituting a whole new organ from them in a test tube. Such a replacement organ would not be rejected upon installation since its cells belong in that particular body. A major benefit of this procedure is that it will get around the problem of the limited supply of potential donors. However, some tricky problems must be solved in order to develop this technique.

When a sperm and an egg unite to form the fertilized cell from which each individual arises, that first cell contains all the information needed to specify every detail about that particular individual. But as that cell divides to produce two, then four, then eight, then 16 cells, some of the information is disregarded in a process we call "differentiation." In fact, it is now estimated that about 80 per cent of the potential genetic information is disregarded in a cell which serves as a mature kidney, heart or lung cell. The problem will be to induce the cells in a test tube to "recall" the information they had at the time of conception. At the moment it is possible to grow a few human tissues in a test tube, but in most cases the cells become abnormal after a few cell divisions; in particular, they lack the organization that would be found in an organ. Thus we must find out how to control the differentiation process itself. Recently a group working with plant—not animal—cells was able to change the differentiation pattern by the use of chemicals; unfortunately, they could not reduplicate their results from experiment to experiment. We have a long way to go in this area, but we do have promising techniques with which to work.

The dilemma associated with such developments should, however, be obvious. If we can give people an almost indefinite stay of death, should they not only have the right to choose to live but also the right to choose their time of dying? In other words, what is immortality? Is it to be an indefinite stay of life here on earth, or is it to be something reserved for the life hereafter?

The Population Explosion

Independent of the above developments, we will soon have to ask whether people should have the right to live indefinitely and thus prevent others from having any life at all—or at least from having a fruitful one. Even without the advent of "spare parts," many of us are convinced that the most serious problem facing us on a worldwide basis is the population explosion.

At present the increase in population is 2 per cent

a year. If we put this number into the compound-interest formula, we can predict how many people there will be at any given time in the future. For example, population will double in 35 years; if we continue at this same rate, in 500 to 600 years there will be one square yard per person on earth. Look at what this means. If we were to stack people at the rate of one person per square yard, all the 3.5 billion people now living on the earth could be crowded into the corporate limits of Chicago; in 500 to 600 years this would be the situation over the whole world. In 1,700 years the mass of people would exceed the mass of the earth. And if we were to provide platforms on which to procreate, in about 6,000 years the mass of people would exceed the mass of the known universe.

These numbers are meant not to amuse but to suggest as simply as possible just how desperate the situation is. Those who say that the population explosion can be disregarded, or that it will take care of itself, are talking not only nonsense but dangerous nonsense. Obviously, something must be done.

Occasionally I hear someone say: "The good Lord put me here, the good Lord will look after me. Therefore, he'll solve this problem without my help." I too believe the good Lord put me here, but he also gave me eyes and a brain to use to avoid catastrophe. Those eyes and brain tell me that in the past there have been only three ways by which animal populations have controlled themselves: (1) starvation (already almost half of the world's population is in a serious state of malnutrition); (2) pestilence (it was the advent of antibiotics which essentially wiped out plagues of all sorts and led to the tremendous increase in human population); (3) predation (man serves as his own predator when he wages war).

Personally I reject all of these as solutions to the problem of overpopulation. What are the alternatives?

There are in the end only two ways to control population. One—increasing the death rate—isn't terribly attractive to most of us. The other is to decrease the birth rate. Although there are a number of means by which this can be done, the main point to consider is that we *must* begin to say, "That child shall not be conceived so that this child can have a fruitful life." Accordingly, we must consider the question: What might that child's life have been if it had been conceived? And we are back to the same questions I have been raising all along.

Prevention of Birth Defects

The fourth area in which tremendous breakthroughs have been and are being made is human genetics. Since success in this area could allow us to control—for better or for worse—many other aspects of human life, the scientific developments and the ethical implications as well are particularly critical not only for individuals but for all of society.

Each year I receive numerous inquiries from parents wanting to know the chances of their having an abnormal child. I cite one example. A couple wrote that their second child had been diagnosed as having cystic fibrosis; they wanted to know what their chances were of having another such child, as well as what dangers were in store for the offspring of their supposedly normal first child. We could give answers to both questions. CF is a so-called recessive trait, which means that children thus afflicted have two defective genes which are the cause of the condition; they receive one such gene from each parent. But in this case neither parent had CF; each had one good and one bad gene for this trait. Thus if they have additional children the chances at each pregnancy are one in four that the child will have two good genes, two in four that like its parents it will have one good and one bad gene, one in four that it will have two bad genes. That is, there is a 25 per cent probability that each future child will not have proper ligament formation and so will have trouble walking and using its arms and legs, that it will have seriously inadequate digestion, that it will have a large accumulation of fluid in its lungs, that it will be highly susceptible to infection, and that it will require at least $200 a month for medical assistance if it is to survive even into its teens.

We can now give similar precise information for more than 500 physical defects. In some cases the repeat chances are one in four, but in others it may be one in two or one in three. Further, we can clinically test for 19 different recessive genes even before the first defective child is born. Unfortunately, these tests are not as refined as we would like; only in six or seven of them are we able to arrive at an answer almost every time. The tests to determine if a person has one good and one bad CF gene yield a definite answer in only about 60 per cent of the cases.

The major point to be made is that we are learning more and more about the unconceived child. In our society we believe—and, I think, properly so—that once a child is conceived it has the right, except in unusual circumstances, not to be aborted. Once a child is born it acquires all kinds of rights and privileges guaranteed by our laws—again, properly so. But an unconceived individual is a hypothetical nothing; it has no rights. Yet we can now predict a good deal about that child. Thus we need to ask: Should an unconceived individual have any rights? In particular, should some unconceived individuals have the right never to be conceived at all? If so, who should look after their rights—since those rights will conflict with the right of the parents to procreate no matter what. Again we must return to our original questions. If we decide that a potential child has the right not to be conceived, we had better be quite sure what that child might have accomplished had it been conceived.

The Possibility of Prior Action

Many of us hope that we can get around this dilemma by modifying heredity in such a way as to prevent congenital abnormalities before they occur. Here is where we stand at present: We know that the heredity of all cells is determined by their nucleic acid (DNA). Currently the heredity of bacteria can be manipulated; one can take a strain of bacteria, grind it up, extract its DNA, put it in another kind of bacteria with quite different properties, and some bacteria of the second type will be transformed, will take on the properties of the first. In other words we have given them a new blueprint, or perhaps we should say a new chemical IBM card.

Such transformation cannot now take place in a controlled way in the case of human beings. However, all of us have had cells transformed by viruses, which are nothing more than packaged nucleic acid. Viruses come in a variety of forms, shaped sometimes like a long rod, sometimes like a diamond, sometimes like a lollipop with the DNA located in the head. When such a virus approaches a cell, it attaches itself tail first and dissolves a hole in the cell wall, after which the DNA is injected (or perhaps slurped) inside. The DNA moves to the nucleus of the cell, where it acts like a "change order." In other words we now have a new chemical IBM card which says, "Hold everything; change the output of this factory."

Usually the transformation turns out to be a lousy one; we get a snuffly nose or a fever blister or polio or even leukemia. But if we can ever come to understand how our chemical IBM card (DNA) exerts its control over the cell's functioning, theoretically we should be able to bring about desirable transformations. It seems unlikely that we shall be able to accomplish such transformations in an adult. For one thing, since each of us has 10^{12} cells, there is little chance of getting the necessary corrective "messages" into each cell. It is also unlikely that we can make a new brain for a mongoloid or an anencephalic. This means that the worst abnormalities should be corrected prior to conception. Approaching the problem by way of the sperm looks like a bad bet; since more than 100 million sperms are given off in one ejaculation, the chances of getting the necessary information into all of them are small. A better approach would probably be by way of the ovaries. At puberty the female possesses all the 100,000 eggs which constitute her lifetime supply, and in her lifetime she will ovulate only from 500 to 1,000 of these. So if we could introduce the necessary corrections into this relatively small number of cells, theoretically we could prevent at least some abnormalities. But in order to make the complex decisions needed in this area we must again return to the question: What would we like for man to be? The emphasis is on "we"; the child can have no say in the matter, since it is not yet conceived.

At this point it is important to realize that whenever science has in the past forced society to face up to the questions: What is man? Why is he here?, it has done a poor job of it. When Copernicus insisted that the earth is not the center of the universe but only a speck of dust, people said this concept could not be true since it downgraded man—and we had a century of controversy. Then along came Darwin to hold that man was not created from a ball of clay but rather evolved through many millions of years; again, people said this too constituted a downgrading of man and thus could not be so. It is to be hoped that we are at the end of the 125 years of that controversy.

Our Responsibility

Obviously science is today generating another controversy, but this time it will be quite different. Instead of downgrading man, science is literally forcing man to play God. And—make no mistake about it—we do play God all the time. Every time we spray a garden with pesticide and so drive away the worms and the robins, we are playing God. Every time a surgeon picks up a scalpel to correct a physical defect in a person, he is playing God. In fact, we all exist because two people played God—they created a life. Thus we are not talking about something new; rather, we are moving from the minor to the major leagues in terms of our ability to control man and his destiny.

Perhaps the most crucial factor in religion's relation to these new developments is the speed with which it addresses itself to their implications. In many scientific areas today knowledge doubles every seven to ten years. Very probably many of the things I have mentioned as possibilities will be realities in 25 or at most 100 years. And although it may be 25 years before we have to make decisions in some areas, prompt action is called for; we must move resolutely within the next five-year period to set up the proper apparatus for decision-making.

In many states critical choices about how decisions are to be made will be decided in the next two or three years. In 1966 bills were introduced into more than 20 state legislatures to change the abortion laws. In fact, three states—Colorado, California and North Carolina—have already enacted legislation which permits a mother plus the district attorney (in cases of rape and incest) or a mother plus three physicians (when the mother's life or health is in danger or when there is a risk of serious defect in the child) to decide on abortion.

Such "juries," I feel, are not adequate to decide on the disposition of a human life. Abortion rarely involves strictly medical questions. An aborted mother is likely to have psychological problems; there are legal complications and moral questions; the whole structure of society is involved, since the decision involves controlling the quality of life either of the mother or of the child. Accordingly, in my own state of Michigan I have recommended that we extend the circumstances in which parents can request and receive authorization for an abortion, *but* that these decisions be made by local boards composed of elected representatives of the medical profession, of psychiatry, of the legal profession, of the clergy and of the public at large. Whether my suggestion is sound is not the main point at issue; I cite it as an illustration of the kinds of questions to be faced right now and in the next few years.

The question is not whether these developments will come but who will decide how to put them to use. In particular, how must the church become involved if it is to carry out its proper function? Suppose, for example, my "jury" arrangement is initiated in your state; how many church people will participate? Only if many are willing to stand up and be counted will religion have much to say about controlling the quality of life and determining what man should be.

Some out of honest conviction, others to avoid responsibility, will say that man must never be so arrogant as to try to decide the quality of life. Perhaps man is here on earth to dance unthinking at the end of a string, like a marionette. If so, then we had better stop much of our current medical practice which cheats normal death, which prevents infants from being naturally aborted and so makes it likely that they will pass their defects on to the next generation. I dissent from that concept; I think

God gave us a brain to help us decide what man should evolve toward. Thus if we are to "increase in wisdom and stature and in favor with God and man" we had better use our God-given brains while there is still time. We earn our right to be heard in the future by responsible action now!

WHAT MAN CAN MAKE OF MAN

Genetic programing could put an end to the biological diversity that has done so much to enrich man's life.

KARL H. HERTZ

Genealogists of thought, unless they are extreme purists, must consider biologists and sociologists kinsmen of some sort, perhaps even kissing cousins. For a fairly recent ancestor common to them all is Charles Darwin, and behind him loom the figures of Thomas Malthus and Adam Smith. Herbert Spencer, who found in evolutionary theory an all-encompassing formula to explicate principles for all forms of life, individual and collective, served as the intellectual progenitor of several lineages of sociologists, from William Graham Sumner, that passionate iconoclast and nay-sayer, to the optimistic Reform Darwinist Lester F. Ward, apostle of progressive social development.

More instructive for our purposes than the use of biological concepts for sociological theory-building, however, are the social policies derived from biological teachings and the appeal to "science" for the legitimation of far-reaching political decisions. Evolutionary theory and early Galtonian doctrines of heredity furnished the bases for the eugenics movement and racialist theories and, specifically, for the development of the immigrant exclusion policies of the United States.

My paramount concern is not to chide the biologists

Dr. Hertz is professor of sociology at Wittenberg University, Springfield, Ohio.

for the uses made of rather primitive knowledge; nor am I interested in doing penance for the sins of the early sociologists. What is important as regards early heredity theory is the attempt to institutionalize these findings of science into a set of social practices, most obviously in the sterilization laws of a number of states, less obviously in the ways, often diverse, in which some of these findings have been handled in the political arena. Here we have a primitive paradigm of how science becomes incorporated into social practice.

Who Will Guard the Guardians?

Today's advances in biology—specifically the growing understanding of the genetic code and the increasing skill in synthesizing life, to mention only two areas of rapidly accelerating knowledge—raise issues of population control fraught with consequences far more revolutionary than either the earlier interventions of the eugenists or the exclusions of the ethnocentrists. In the light of these revolutionary possibilities we must ask the biologists not only what man can make of man but also who shall be the trustee of these powers. And who will guard the guardians?

Scientists, for good reasons, prefer to view their discipline from within. Their primary interest lies in safeguarding freedom of research and the disciplined elaboration of ideas. For most of them the world of science is autonomous, ascetically dedicated to truth, governed by impersonal and universal norms according to which ideas are screened and new discoveries elaborated. The administration and public use of the findings of science are not normally part of that world.

But science can no longer avoid the issues connected with the translation of its findings into social practice. The question is not the employment of science in the construction of world views, nor is it the forays made by philosophers and liberal clergymen to appropriate scientific categories for their own use: these, scientists can disavow and ignore. But there is a form of institutionalizing science whose existence depends on science. The very nature of the institutionalization, the translation of scientific knowledge into social practice, carries normative consequences.

Science as Society's Servant

No science can really escape being a servant of society. Each science as it has developed has provided the basis for one or more technologies—bridges from "pure science" to the everyday affairs of men. Some of these technologies have had far-reaching consequences for the daily routines of human life. Medicine offers an immediate example of application of biological knowledge. The use of ecology in conservation is an equally important if less obvious example. Early eugenics was a primitive effort in the same direction, an effort which largely failed.

Scientists may disavow as foreign to science the values to which many of the eugenists appealed. But this disclaimer does not dispose of the issue, for at the moment when a scientist or any other person perceives that a given scientific discovery has a human application, certain inescapable questions arise: on whom and under what conditions shall this discovery be used, and to what kinds of social goals should it be instrumental. Scientists themselves rarely preside over the application of their findings. Rather, it is persons scientifically trained to some degree, sometimes minimal, who act as the executors of science in its social application, with or without the help of lay boards, office clerks and others whose knowledge and insight may be quite limited. That is, our problem is not one of science but of the technologies derived from it.

Technologies may be viewed as ways in which science is "socialized." Alongside the community of pure scientists, often intermingled with it, there grows up a community of professional practitioners which, like all communities, develops its codes of ethics. These codes differ from the codes of "pure science" at one important point. For while the latter codes quite properly center on the protection of objectivity, the focal point of professional codes is "right conduct," i.e., maintaining the integrity of professional practice. They offer guidelines for the use of knowledge.

The ethic that develops—this point must be underscored—is not derived from the scientific findings. When we consider social policy, we must recognize that scientists may in their prescription of what is "good" for man be expressing the prejudices of their upbringing or their commitment to a Platonic political ideology in which they are the philosopher-kings who can shape the future. In raising questions about the competence of biologists to determine the optimal genotype, I am not impugning their scientific knowledge; I am pointing out that when one moves from knowledge to practice, one inevitably becomes entangled in questions that are not really scientific. That is, to prescribe the genetic constitution of the man of the future, to bring him into being via sperm banks and genetic surgery, is to claim to know what the ideal human being ought to be like. This is not biology but ethics and moral philosophy.

In one sense ethics is inescapable when a science is "socialized" into a technology. We can and must always ask: What legitimates the moral concerns of the biotechnician, the fellow who will carry out these programs? Where do—and where shall—his values come from? Similarly, we must ask what justifies turning the application of genetics to improve the species in ways which do not interfere with human freedom into an imperialistic program that would presumably eliminate all but a few human genotypes. Even granting that this would be an evolutionary advantage—a question that must remain open—who is so wise that he can make the choice?

The possibilities of remaking what evolution has thus far brought into being go far beyond the improvement of the human species; they include the reshaping of the human environment. But this is a different question from the one on which I wish to concentrate. The issue is most urgent with respect to man. Technologically much of what Professor H. J. Muller suggests—notably in his *Studies in Genetics* (Indiana University Press, 1962)— is already practicable or will very soon be so. Hence, we must raise not only the question of policy but also the political question: how shall the execution of this program be organized?

Without laboring the point—leaving out all sorts of questions—we must ask, for example, who shall decide whose sperm is to be deposited in the sperm bank? Or, later on, whose ova shall be chosen? As a practicing politician, I know that research scientists and Nobel prize winners rarely sit on local boards of public affairs. These positions fall to the comparatively less informed, to people not always uncorruptible and unprejudiced; and, in addition, the daily routine is usually in the hands of clerk-typists and secretaries. If Thomas Jefferson was right when he said in his letter to John Adams that Whig and Tory are terms belonging to natural history, shall we also exclude Goldwater Republicans—and, in the age of the great consensus, perhaps Kennedy Democrats— from being depositors in the First National Sperm Bank of Bloomington, Indiana? Do we really want to run the political risks of programing human heredity?

Threshold of a Revolution

In this connection we may well ask two questions: The first, put quite cold-bloodedly, is: Can we avoid it? The late John von Neumann once said that whatever is technologically possible will be done. Genetic programing is a distinct possibility, not nearly as remote as laymen would like to believe.

Granted that we undertake this programing: what then of the evolutionary effects—first, the effects with respect to man; second, the effects with respect to the social order?

In another context J. Bronowski has asked: "What truths can be stable in the soul of man, so easily mutilated, by nature so changeable?" If the millenniums from Neanderthal days to the present have worked changes in man; if indeed, as sociologists teach, the character of man is covariant with his social and cultural milieu, then these changes have generally come with glacier-like slowness. They have represented evolutionary selection and adaptation without the self-conscious direction of man.

Today the situation has changed drastically. We may be standing on the threshold of a major revolution in human history, biological and social. Turning the clock back has never been a successful response to a revolution. We must instead turn to other questions.

For the most part the development of codes of professional ethics has been a "natural" process of growth, as unconscious as the evolutionary process itself. Indeed, as historians of science know, Darwinian biology and Manchester economics shared common viewpoints as to the immutable autonomy of the processes of nature. Laissez-faire seemed of necessity the proper rule for both realms, since man's powers of intervention not only were meager but their employment was fundamentally imprudent. To "let nature take its course" was to guarantee the best outcome. Often calling upon evolutionary theory for legitimation, a whole school of political economists made laissez-faire its battle cry.

Today we cannot entrust the development of new codes of professional ethics to the vagaries of random cultural developments. Doubly so, because in earlier times the Western nations, where technologies flourished, possessed a high degree of consensus on many matters of human conduct. But "moral philosophy" has become rudderless, and our century is marked by cultural heterogeneity. Under these conditions, what results from the chance cross-fertilization of science and culture may be destructive, if not lethal, in its consequences.

A 'Brave New World'?

Can we successfully institutionalize the process of biotechnical change? Or perhaps—since we know that there will be some kind of institutionalization—we should ask: What kinds of values will be dominant in the professional codes of the biotechnicians? Never before has the pressure of technological change pushed so hard against the norm-generating capacity of a social order. "Genetic programing" may be a development of the same historic proportions as atomic energy. We are now faced with programs of implementation. Some of the programers even seem to know what the genetic constitution of the "ideal man" of the future should be. But do they, do we really know? By what criteria is this ideal man to be determined? Must not religious, ethical and political considerations weigh as heavily as biological ones in our reflections as to whether we ought to take this step? Coping with these questions may require among biologists a breakthrough as radical as the one which led to

establishment of the *Bulletin of the Atomic Scientists.*
Let me draw upon medicine for an analogy. Central to
medical ethics, especially in the borderline instance of
euthanasia, has been respect for the patient as a person.
Norms requiring consent for surgical procedure, etc., indicate that, with whatever shortcomings, medicine at
its best does not manipulate human organisms as things.

Moreover, "genetic programing" is not the only possibility. We must also accept the fact that life can be
brought into being in the laboratory. At present all these
developments are, of course, still extremely primitive.
But can we rule out the "brave new world" in which
"man" can come into being in an "artificial womb"?

In short, is man really ready to play God? This is not
just the general question whether man ought to have the
right to manipulate his own biological constitution. What
is crucial is that one set of men, the biotechnicians, will
be intervening in the lives of other people, determining the traits of other people's children, presenting "parents" with children not of their own "procreation." The
objects of this programing—in whatever form it is carried
out—may easily turn out to be the poor and the power-
less, presumably of "inferior" stock. For any application
of this knowledge will take place within the framework
of the existing distributions of power and privilege. Specifically, my question is not primarily whether genetic
programing and other developments will come, but under what conditions and limitations, with what protection of human rights and prudent constraint of utopian-
ism. How shall limits and directions be set? Even: How
does the creature-become-creator understand himself,
his powers and his responsibilities?

These are not science-fiction issues. We must ask in
all seriousness: What can man make of man? Where
shall the normative decisions lie? What about the consequences for what we know as the human family? Who

shall frame the code of ethics for the biotechnicians?
Who is competent to define the "ideal man"?

Recent philosophical discussions among scientists—
e.g., Michael Polanyi and, in this context, John Platt—
stress the degree to which man, that rather defective
species we know and are, shapes the world through his
knowing and doing. These discussions may foreshadow
a new understanding of man as person, as participant in
the process of discovery. At the same time, they imply a
rejection of many of the behavioristic and mechanistic
concepts of man that are now taken for granted.

Defending Against Dehumanization

Still we ask: Who is man? Which conception of man
will determine how and when we apply the biotechnical
skills we are developing? This is not an obscurantist argument against technology. It is a question of how policy shall be made under conditions of knowledge constantly subject to revision and correction.

What can man make of man? Does the answer not
finally rest on the understanding of man which develops
within a technical community? It is a fact that preoccupation with the "objective accounts" of human illness
and with the physiology and chemistry of the human
organism often predisposes doctors of medicine to see
man in less than personal terms. The professional requirements of "objectivity" and "impersonality"—norms
that are indispensable—tend to transform the patient into
a complicated piece of malfunctioning machinery. Perhaps the conservatism inherent in the Hippocratic oath
has been one of our defenses against the dehumanization of medicine.

But as we cross new frontiers we leave behind the
traditions that informed our thinking. A great deal may
depend on where the weights fall. For example, René

Dubos and other biologists insist that we must attend to the ways in which man differs from his near relatives, not just to the ways in which he is like them; for it is in the differences that the uniqueness of man is found. The biotechnician would set up one kind of program if he shared this view, another if he held anti-Dubos ideas.

Moral Neutrality: Hazardous Luxury

If the technician also takes seriously the insights into human behavior contributed by some branches of the behavioral sciences—insights as to the depths of personality and the role of the symbolic and the unconscious —then the professional code developed may be quite different from the code based on doctrines of mechanism and behaviorism. Above all, if the biotechnician, along with the behavioral scientist, accepts the proposition that we are still far from understanding man, the development of biotechnics will surely take another tack. To begin programing on the assumption that all the evidence is in could have tragic consequences. Nor may we be able to undo the consequences. To be sure, our immigration laws have been amended—but it hasn't been easy.

What will man make of man? One of the glories of our species—despite all the heartache attendant on living— has been the diversity within it. This diversity—both of genetic endowment and of cultural development—has contributed much to man's spread over the planet and, I would argue, to the richness of life in every society. Biological diversity is a kind of counterpart of political pluralism. But will not the biotechnicians be tempted to shape us according to a few patterns they prefer? All questions of norms aside, what will this limited patterning do to man's capacity to survive as a biological organism?

As a sociologist, I also have what I consider a legitimate question which arises from a professional preoccupation. Will not "genetic programing" lead us again to overemphasize the role of heredity in human development? Do we not face a serious problem in personality theory at this point? Is there not a tendency among some geneticists to treat the question of personality development as almost exclusively a biological given?

It seems to me that the biologist cannot much longer afford the luxury of "moral neutrality." In Darwinism's heyday biologists, philosophers and popularizers alike seized upon evolution as the basis for a new ethic. I would not be so brazen as to recommend a repetition of this undertaking. But I would suggest that in an open universe, where the evolutionary process is one agent of change, we must—now that we have reached the point of self-conscious direction of the process—ask ethical questions of a kind that cannot be answered without the counsel of the biologists, indeed of the best of them. The nuclear physicists could not turn over the application of atomic power to the engineers; no more will the biologists be able to turn their new knowledge over to the biotechnicians.

If what is unique about man is his "personhood"—man as a self-conscious center of action—must we not incorporate this as a constant into our biotechnology? And how?

It may very well be true—I believe it is—that the content of science, any science, does not in and of itself validate an ethic. In this sense it is quite obvious that our works do not save us. The basic moral affirmations needed to shape the ethical codes for the employment of our biological knowledge will need a different kind of validation. Here the affirmations of faith must count; and the kinds of communities of faith men belong to may be decisive.

Perhaps even this question thus becomes inescapable for the biologist as he ponders what man can make of man.

THE CHURCHES AND EVOLUTION

Unless Christian institutions share in and speak to man's common destiny, they have no legitimate claim to existence.

PHILIP HEFNER

The greatest danger for the churches in the dialogue between science and religion is the temptation to stand on the sidelines, watching their corps of theologians engage the scientific community. This spectator role is particularly tempting in the discussion of evolution, since as institutions which encompass the broad masses of people the churches assume that relatively few of their members will ever confront the issues of evolution posed by the biological and anthropological sciences in the sophisticated form articulated by the scientists and theologians.

This spectator attitude simply reveals that the churches do not comprehend the real issues of the dialogue in general, of the discussion of evolution in particular. The issues of evolution touch the fundamental patterns of development in which the churches as institutions and all their members as persons participate—no matter what the level of their sophistication. When the churches recognize this they will have to move very quickly off the sidelines and into the thick of the discussion.

Several kinds of issues confront the churches in the dis-

Dr. Hefner is associate professor of systematic theology, Lutheran School of Theology, Chicago, Ill.

cussion of evolution. Some have to do with concrete ethical dilemmas which arise out of new methods of technology; others pertain to the theological rearrangements which these ethical dilemmas demand; still others are highly theoretical, pertaining to the churches' relation to culture. At the risk of diffuseness I shall touch on all of these, so as to indicate the breadth of the implications evolution has for the churches.

Changing Concepts of 'Man'

The most startling impact of the biological sciences today is their assault on conventional notions of what it means to be man, of what it means to live and die. The procedures of man's change and evolution have been so radically recast by the learning and technology of our age, specifically by biotechnology, that the old understandings of humanity, life and death simply do not obtain in the way they once did. A few sensational data will establish this point:

What does it mean to be man, when the heights and depths of human emotion (the emotional range worthy of an Oedipus Rex or a Lear) can be manipulated by chemicals or by electrical charges? What does it mean to be man when asexual reproduction of life is foreseeable? What do life and death mean in an age when resuscitation of the heart, transplanting of organs and employment of certain drugs make it possible to maintain heart and lung activity indefinitely? For centuries the "mirror test" (holding a mirror to a man's mouth in order to detect breath of life) served as a legal definition of death; today, physicians speak in terms of the state of a man's brain (revealed by various tests) as the definition—since certain kinds of brain damage render life nothing more than "vegetable existence" regardless of the state of heart and lung activity. What does this do to theological concepts of life and death? What do human development and achievement become if it proves feasible to manipulate intelligence through genetic engineering, or if memory can be improved through injections?

That some of these developments are decades, even generations, away from perfection does not detract from the clear implication that the biological sciences have—through their technology—radically altered our conception of what it means to be man and what it means to live and die. It is the factors of *control* and *manipulation* that figure most in upsetting previous conceptions of man. Precisely because they encompass broad masses of people whose daily lives are influenced mightily by prevailing conceptions of what it means to live and die, the churches have no choice but to take biotechnology seriously in their theology of man and in their preaching about and to man.

In some ways the traditional Christian understandings are extremely pertinent to our new understandings of man. For example, Christian faith has never equated life with physical longevity; rather, it has understood that the *quality* of human existence is pre-eminent over its *length*. Does this mean that euthanasia is distinctly commensurate with Christian doctrine? Christian faith has also understood, under the rubric of "ongoing creation," that God continues his creative activity in every age. Does this mean that human manipulation of emotions, memory, growth and development, life and death is somehow God's creative will? It would certainly be difficult to ascribe to God's creativity the experiments performed by Hitler's doctors in the 1940s, but perhaps that creativity seems more obvious in the experiments being performed in mental hospitals today, or in the genetic engineering which may in the years ahead eliminate muscular dystrophy or sickle-celled anemia.

This is not the place to offer answers for such questions and dilemmas. It is enough to assert here that the issues raised by biotechnology are significant for the day-to-day theology and preaching that mark the life of the churches. The character of that theology and preaching will have a marked influence on laymen who are daily responsible for resolving the new dilemmas (physicians, for example, who must determine rationally which patients shall live and which shall be neglected). And it will determine what role pastors and congregations play in forming public policy. No single dimension of our doctrine of man, for example, is untouched by the fact that rage, lust, euphoria and contentment can be induced at will by human manipulators, just as our doctrine of God is reshaped by awareness that God has permitted man to remold the natural order.

Foundations for the Dialogue

When the churches begin to rethink their theology and preaching about man in the light of the technology of the biological sciences and when they formulate social-ethical policy in accordance with that theology and preaching, other issues, even larger and more amorphous, will emerge. As they engage in day-to-day theologizing, preaching and ethical planning, as they attend in detail to the discussion of evolutionary theory as a whole, the churches become aware that they are not alone in their concern, that they share a bond with other men and other groups, a bond with all of man's cultural forms within the fundamental processes of life. The churches participate in the universal life process just as do all other forms; the evolutionist reminds them that they stand with all other human forms deeply embedded within a cultural milieu out of which they have emerged and in intercourse with which they have pursued their destinies.

For the churches to be so embedded within a culture means that they share in that culture's response to what Julian H. Steward (in an earlier chapter) calls the circumstances which activate its inherent but hitherto latent genius. The churches are co-products, along with other human forms, of the cultural processes which have enabled man to reach his present level of development. Whether or not they wish to acknowledge it, they are part of the evolution of culture which serves the purpose of rendering it possible for man to be what we consider human and to develop even more complex and, hopefully, satisfactory forms of human being.

Confrontation with the fundamental relatedness between church and culture compels the churches to be more modest, realistic and self-conscious about their roles in society. This is not simply an affirmation of the cultural determinedness of the churches; more important, it is a reminder that the theories of the cultural evolutionists call attention to the matrix within which the churches carry out their life and mission. If the churches are communities of redemption or if they are beholden for their existence to some sort of divine revelation, it is perfectly clear that that redemption and divine revelation are incarnate within the forms, aspirations and teleology of the culture in which those churches exist.

Furthermore, if we accept evolutionary theory, these cultural forms, aspirations and teleology do not exist autonomously for their own sake; rather, they exist for the development of the processes of life or, more specifically, for the sake of refining and developing and maintaining human life. Far from challenging the transcendence of redemption and revelation, the assertion of cultural embeddedness reminds us that such transcendence cannot be defined in terms of distance or "otherness" from the processes of life. Revelation and redemption are described in terms of the intensification, or even the perfection, of the authentic purpose of life in any given time or place, an intensification and perfection that only God can actualize. As such, the revelation which constitutes the churches has come in, with and under the power of evolution. And when that revelation asserts a kind of pre-eminence over the life process itself, it is a pre-eminence from within, a pre-eminence rooted in the basis of creation.

Transcendence Offers an Option

If divine revelation and redemption are incarnate within the realities described by the evolutionary theorists, it is inevitable that they will be construed as options (perhaps the only real options) for the fulfillment of human destiny. To deny that our faith pertains inherently to the consummation of our destiny as human beings is to insist on a rupture between the churches and the fundamental processes of life-development which at best is unintelligible and at worst grotesque.

Within this framework the cliché that "Christian faith is a message about man's true humanity" appears to be unassailable, since the communities of the churches participate in the processes of life's evolution that make human existence what it is and since their message concerns itself with man's profoundest option for the authentic fulfillment of existence. This is not an authoritarian claim by the churches. For they know well that often there is no discernible empirical difference between the humanity of Christians and that of non-Christians, and that men *do* come to full, authentic humanity outside the church, while those inside often fall far short of the mark of humanity. Nevertheless, Christians believe that, as Michael Novak recently put it, "men seeking to be men are at least very like what Jesus reveals them to be." That is, even though there are a plurality of ways to achieve authentic humanity, the Jesus Christ who is honored in the churches is the fulfillment of that humanity.

In a passive sense, this suggests that the churches have received much, and continue to receive much, from their cultural milieu. They have received the total background against which they live out their careers, as well as the possibilities within which they can stake out their goals. They must inevitably acknowledge their debt to culture, not with regret or with the pragmatic notion that cultural forms are simply the inescapable target toward which their missionary strategy must be aimed, but with readiness to acknowledge that the shapes and thrusts of their culture are intrinsic to their life, that indeed culture *is* their life (as Tillich reminded us when he said that "culture is the form of religion, religion the substance of culture").

Cultural processes and tendencies are not patterns imposed from without, to which the churches must conform their strategies; these processes and tendencies inform the churches' life from within, and they constitute the lineaments according to which the life of the churches expresses itself. The churches need not hesitate to make this assertion, because they believe that God created those cultural processes.

In an active sense, cultural evolution is something to which the churches can make a positive and creative contribution on the basis of the insights which derive from revelation and redemption, a contribution which they believe can stand as an option for the development of man's life. This does not mean that they simply legitimize whatever forms and purposes are currently available for cultural development. In fact, their very participation in the teleology of their culture may be the basis for critique and protest (as, for example, the German churchmen's protest against Hitler). Certain forms and purposes appear to be deleterious, even disastrous—unworthy of man's human being and even fatal for it. The churches believe that God's revelation discloses the truest and profoundest destiny for man, a destiny which cultural processes can (at least momentarily) thwart and reject. But that revelation does not pull man away from the biological and cultural evolutionary processes that have made him; on the contrary, revelation enables man to share in the consummation of those processes.

The inseparable relatedness of the churches and their cultural milieu points to a second affirmation which underlies the argument of the preceding paragraphs. It is a bifocal affirmation: (1) The redemption which is cradled in the life of the churches is the fulfillment of the life processes which the evolutionary theorist describes, and as such the "Christian faith cannot ever be in conflict with any of the historical forms of the building of the earthly city, to the extent that these forms are authentically human";* (2) the life processes which stand at the center of evolutionary theory cannot fulfill their destiny apart from obedience to the God who created life. As Karl Rahner has put it, "An integral humanism requires the experience of God."**

Evolution of life—biological and cultural—aims at the maintenance and refinement of life, and so far as we now know that life is pre-eminently human. The churches are both free and under the imperative to present themselves as communities which seek to actualize the most adequate options for the development of human life. But they insist that man's most authentic evolution is inclusive of the affirmation of God, whose purpose has set evolution in motion and whose redemption aims at its fulfillment. This bifocal affirmation is a fundamental

* Quoted in Roger Garaudy, "The Marxist-Christian Dialogue: Possibilities, Problems, Necessity," *Continuum*, 3:408–9 Winter 1966.

** *Ibid.*, page 408.

assumption which guides the theologian or preacher who tries to speak meaningfully to a world caught up in the new biotechnology.

Implications for the Christian Community

The line of argument I have unfolded thus far indicates that *the issues which emerge from evolutionary theory make their most significant thrust at the substance of the churches' life and preaching.* That is, as the churches face the issues posed by evolution they discover that fostering high-level dialogue between scientists and theologians is only one level of their response, and perhaps a secondary level at that. Important as such dialogue may be, it is a problematic enterprise, at least in this country, and considering the magnitude of the issues at stake for our culture the number of working scientists and theologians involved in it is surprisingly small. Furthermore, the range of the dialogue is disappointingly narrow, reaching out only occasionally beyond a relatively small group of interested intellectuals. Important as the methodology of dialogue is, it is even more urgent today for the churches to concentrate their efforts at the second level of response to evolution—that of their substantial life and preaching.

At the level of methodology theologians and philosophers seek to refine their conceptualities. This involves analysis of how men know, and whether "scientific" knowing and religious knowing are identical, antithetical or otherwise commensurable. It also involves detailed scrutiny of the language used by religion and science in order to understand how the one compares with the other, as well as investigation into the philosophical presuppositions underlying the scientific endeavor in order to determine whether it is open to the consideration of the ultimate realities to which theology's attention is directed. Finally, the dialogue seeks to determine whether the concerns and formulations of theology have any intelligible correlate within the scientific purview.

The second level, that on which the substance of the churches' life and preaching is involved, in many ways presupposes the intellectual efforts of the first. But it is quite distinct, and its goals and methods must not be confused with those of the first. For at this level the churches are involved in shaping the basic patterns and content of their common life in the light of what the biological and cultural evolutionary theorists are telling us. Out of this common life emerge the theology, preaching and ethical planning mentioned above. In comparison with the dialogue, this shaping of life and preaching aims at a different audience and pursues different goals. The churches shape their life and preaching in order to touch the millions of people who come into contact with Christian faith at the level of the ordinary processes of existence which form the loom on which human life is woven. Although not divorced from the problems of conceptual refinement, shaping the churches' impact on the lives of their people is better conceived as a task of gaining insight into the significance of evolution for life and acting upon that insight.

This second level of response is in no sense an anti-intellectual retreat from the rigors of dialogue—indeed, it presupposes its own kind of dialogue. Efforts at this level are rigorous attempts to bring what evolutionary theory says about the processes of life in general to bear upon the specific processes of life that constitute the existence of the churches. They represent an honest attempt to structure the *life* of the Christian communities in response to what men have come to learn generally about life from evolutionary theory.

Such efforts to restructure church life rest on the prior convictions outlined above: that Christian truth is a fulfillment rather than a destruction of natural truth; that God's truth is continuous (not identical) and not discontinuous with what man's best reason has discovered about man himself. From this perspective we judge that the attempt to bring evolutionary theory to bear upon the churches is an effort to be humanly honest about the life we lead in our concrete communities of faith. This humanly honest effort is an affirmation that the concrete life of our communities of faith is of a piece with all created life. Only so is it possible for the churches to claim that their life represents the redemption of all created life.

What are the issues raised by evolutionary theory, in light of which the churches will want to reshape the substance of their life and preaching? What are the evolutionary theorists telling us that could be pertinent to the communities of Christian faith? The preceding articles in this series have laid before us three basic issues that have deep significance for the life of the churches: freedom, determinism, change. These issues underlie the perplexities posed by biotechnology. Freedom questions whether man has the ability—within his technology—to fulfill his own selfhood; determinism, whether he is the product of what has gone before and of what his environment pressures him to be; change, what kind of continuity exists between tomorrow's needs, today's responses and the heritage of truth from the past.

To say that evolutionary theory makes its impact at the substance of the churches' life and preaching means that life and preaching must enable Christians to find resources within their communities of faith for understanding freedom, determinism and change so as to perceive within those elements God's redemption for their everyday lives. This is not a matter of ecclesiastical evangelistic strategy but rather a challenge to set forth in the empirical communities of faith the Christian options within a world that the evolutionary theorists describe. It is in these communities that men and women conduct their lives under the impact of the realities which those theorists describe; it is there that they carry with them the bewilderment, fear, anxiety, disappointment, despair, hopefulness, anticipation, courage and perseverance that attend freedom, determinism and change. So if they are to find the actuality of God's redemption, it must be in the context of these hopes and fears.

Where Men's Lives Are Lived

To say that evolutionary theory touches men where they actually live means that the churches must challenge, buttress, stimulate and console the common life of men and women who daily wrestle with the processes of freedom, determinism and change. It means that the substance of life and preaching must be shaped with reference to the actual impact of freedom, determinism and change upon men's lives. The most practical consequence will be that everything that takes place within our churches—worship, ethics, education, pastoral counseling—must be a reasonable and honest response to human existence under the impact of these central issues. Otherwise the churches cannot make any intelligible claim upon men today, nor can they assert that theirs are communities of God's redemption.

To put it squarely: To shape life and preaching in the light of evolutionary theory is to seek a rediscovery of the gospel, the Word and grace of God, in the context of freedom, determinism and change, which the evolutionary theorists rightly designate as constitutive for life. These theorists remind the churches that God's Word is irrelevant, that it is not really a word at all if it is not incarnate within the realities of freedom, determinism and change that mark the universal processes of life.

The issue of freedom demands that we proclaim and actualize within the Christian community the possibilities for achieving selfhood in the face of forces that would destroy the self's integrity. Christian freedom is more than indeterminism—the sheer unpredictability of the self's actions—just as it is more than the assertion that the self cannot be reduced to the sum of its parts and the components of its own past and its social context. Freedom is the capacity to achieve integral selfhood, and although—as Langdon Gilkey's article reminds us—this capacity is not sheer autonomy, it must relate positively to the intelligent and constructive participation in the *making* of our own future which technologies of all types set before us today. Freedom must be the capacity and willingness to enter into the making of our future despite the fact that man can now deal death to himself. God's grace in Jesus Christ is a grace that frees us for both the integrity of free selfhood and the shaping of constructive policy for our own future.

Determinism raises the question of God's providence —perhaps the most difficult article of Christian belief. Affirmation of providence entails the excruciatingly uncertain task of discerning God's hand in the affairs of the day; it also entails, in the face of a prevailing secular view that considers freedom and providence to be antitheses, the absurd claim that man's freedom is raised to its highest power in the fulfillment of his destiny under a supremely providential God. As Professor Gilkey has indicated, scientific thought has not succeeded in holding freedom and determinism together in a meaningful way. The churches' preaching may not succeed in doing so either, but Christian life today will be sham if it does not persuasively set forth the perennial Christian conviction that man can accept his destiny because it is formed by the same God who created him free.

The churches must confront the radical discontinuities threatened by the radical movements of change with the affirmation that God himself is at the root of change, and that he himself effects the continuity within all change. The change that is intrinsic to our common life represents the dynamic of God, who is accomplishing his own will and fulfilling his own nature even as he is propelling us toward the consummation of his kingdom. We need not fear change; we can immerse ourselves in it freely because we thereby participate in God himself. At the same time the churches must demonstrate that their traditions can be resources of life within change; rather than being demonic forces which stifle change by their insistence that today must always bear yesterday's stamp of approval, those traditions provide the resources for both freedom and criticism within change.

Closer attention to change and the churches' relationship to it can serve as a paradigm of the churches' relationship to culture as a whole and to the life process which evolutionary theory describes.

Professor Steward asserts that change is "not only accepted but is becoming a goal for its own sake." This is in sharp contrast to previous attitudes which resisted change as a degradation of the Golden Age (remember Henry Adams' *bon mot*: "All that is necessary to refute Evolution is to compare the development in the American presidency from George Washington to U. S. Grant") or which relegated change to the evanescent realm of becoming, from which one ought to escape into the pure realm of being-itself. For most of its history the Christian church has argued that change is not to be considered real in itself but is to be looked on simply as a restatement of the past, the original revelation from Jesus and the apostles. Development of doctrine has always been a difficult pill for Christian theology to swallow, not to mention development of faith or of God.

Time to Acknowledge Change

Evolutionary theory, whether biological or cultural, insists that change is inherent in the very foundation of the life process in which the churches live. So deeply and decisively is change a part of our common life that Professor Steward can write: "Whereas sociocultural systems and values formerly persisted for centuries or even millenniums, one now has to ask how briefly a social system, art form or other component of culture can endure and still be an integral part of the culture." Biotechnology brings the inevitability of this swift change home to us with crushing force.

The churches have not as yet fully acknowledged this decisive character of change. They have not committed themselves wholly to change in even the obvious sectors: civil rights, automation, international relations. As a consequence, much of what they say and do has no meaningful correlation to the present experience of the men and women who come within their orbit. This accounts for a widespread breakdown of confidence within the churches.

On the other hand, in certain selected areas and among certain enclaves where the churches have accepted change, there are vigor, excitement and strong interest in the efforts by Christians to be honest in their relationship with the mainstream of life and in their articulation of redemptive realities within that mainstream. For years some sensational, somewhat superficial programs have been set forth which have sought to propel the churches into the maincurrents of the day's cultural change. Today some very serious attempts are being made to demonstrate that change is intrinsic to God himself and that therefore cultural change can be rooted in his very nature. Names of such men as Leslie Dewart,

Gerhard Ebeling, Jürgen Moltmann, Wolfhart Pannenberg and Schubert Ogden come to mind. Different as are their attempts and uneven as is the quality of their achievements, the aim of all is to show that commitment to change, as Professor Steward describes it and as the biotechnicians implement it, is not a threat to our faith but an avenue for deeper understanding of the God who is affirmed in the Christian tradition.

Professor Steward goes on to say, however: "Change seems to be getting out of hand. Every individual and every nation confront conflicting choices and expectations, and there are no clear guidelines for behavior." He closes his essay on the rather stoic note that change inevitably brings traumatic effects and that the most we can hope to do is to mitigate those effects somewhat.

If participation in the processes of cultural life forces the churches to accept radical change as a constant feature of everyday life, obedience to God's revelation within those life processes compels them also to contribute their own creative suggestions and patterns for establishing guidelines in the midst of change, along with criteria for determining the direction of change. The role of tradition in the life and faith of the Christian community rises all the more importantly, not as a dead monument that seeks to obliterate change but rather as a witness to all men that there is continuity amid change, and that full participation in the tradition actually liberates men to accept change fully and immerse themselves in it.

Such commitment to the problems of guiding cultural change will increasingly occupy the churches' efforts, not as an adjunct to their "religious" activity but as intrinsic to their life. If it is true that feeding myself is a material problem, whereas feeding my neighbor is a spiritual problem, then participation in the decision-making process of guiding the future of biological and cultural evolution is also a spiritual work, since it involves God's destiny for his creation. In this light, urban planning, air pollution, arms control, civil rights, the practice of medicine (and its impact on law) and a great number of other problems become spiritual concerns which the churches cannot avoid when they plan concretely for the allocation of their time and money.

The Christian churches cannot rest with Professor Steward's cautious goals of "mitigating" the traumatic effects of change. Rather, they believe that since God is the Lord and Creator of change, that change will move toward the consummation God has designed. This is the basis of Christian hope—a Christian virtue that may well be judged as an empirical mark of God's presence in the world. The depth and unshakability of Christian hope—in its present and material rather than in an other-worldly form—will drive the churches to cooperate all the more vigorously in efforts to guide cultural change.

The earnest Christian grappling with the problem of man's freedom to face his selfhood amid the flux of cultural change, as well as his confidence that God is the Lord of change, brings together the three major strands of concern within which God's revelation comes to men who live in the midst of the issues that evolutionary theory has framed. When the churches listen obediently to the gospel of man's freedom in Christ under the Lord of history and change, they are participating Christianly in the processes of life evolution in which all men share. They are not distancing themselves from the cultural evolutionary process; rather, they are demonstrating that to be a Christian today is to share in the ultimate destiny of humankind which is relevant for all men living in that process. Their special hope for and special criticism of this process stem from their conviction that Jesus has unfolded the goal and the center of all of life.

If this argument is correct, it seems clear that the task of the churches is to share in and contribute to the common life of our culture. Their life and preaching are misunderstood—both by those inside and by those outside—if they are not recognized simultaneously as part of the thrust of our common life toward its evolutionary end and as part of the ultimate answer as to the destiny of that evolutionary thrust. Biological and cultural evolutionary theory and the technology they have produced confront the churches with an unprecedented testimony to the fact that our faith is part of man's development toward his humanity, and that the consummation we hope for is the ultimate goal of that development.

Until the churches recognize their place in the total evolutionary process of life, they cannot fully appreciate their responsibility or their positive significance in God's world. When they do acknowledge their place in the universal movement of life, they will glimpse the true cosmic implications of the gospel which forms the substance of their existence. They will understand that their commitment to God is a commitment to man. They will understand that if they do not share in and speak to the common destiny of all life, they have no legitimate claim to existence.

THE SIGNIFICANCE OF TEILHARD

His greatest contribution was his concern for the synthesis of evolutionary and Christian thought.

IAN G. BARBOUR

At the center of much of the recent discussion of the religious and ethical implications of evolution is the writing of that remarkable Jesuit paleontologist Pierre Teilhard de Chardin. Teilhard's vision of an evolutionary process whose basic character is spiritual has evoked vehement reactions of both praise and criticism, running the gamut from "the greatest work of the 20th century" to "sheer nonsense." Perhaps we can reach some understanding of these diverse appraisals, and of the underlying issues between evolution and religion, by examining the components of his many-faceted thought.

Teilhard as Evolutionary Scientist

Teilhard's scientific training and work dealt with fossils. His technical papers, some of which are collected in *The Appearance of Man*, are valuable contributions to science. He was offered a chair at the Collège de France (though forbidden by his order to accept it) and was elected to the French Academy of Sciences. His more general works, such as *The Phenomenon of Man*

Dr. Barbour is chairman of the department of religion and professor of physics at Carleton College.

and *The Vision of the Past*, include considerable scientific information descriptive of evolutionary history. Though he gives less attention to biological theories concerning the mechanisms of evolution, he does refer frequently to mutations and natural selection. He recognizes the role of chance and randomness, "the blind fantasy of large numbers in the groping advance of nature." He shares with most scientists the conviction that man is firmly rooted in nature, an integral part of an evolving universe. He avoids one of the major causes of conflict between science and religion in the past—the postulation of divine intervention to explain gaps in the scientific account—by declaring that direction and purpose are displayed in the whole process, not in the special creation of particular creatures.

Nowhere do Teilhard's writings contravene accepted biological theories. He does defend "orthogenesis," but he uses the term in a purely descriptive way to refer to *directionality*, however achieved. Moreover, he says, it must not be assumed that the trend toward greater complexity and consciousness is a simple "straight-line" ascent. He is among the minority of scientists which holds that even lower organisms have a "*within*," a rudimentary responsiveness or sensitivity which is the forerunner of man's mental life. But he does not, like the vitalists, postulate in the material order gaps through which a separate life-principle operates. The "within" is another way of looking at an integral system whose "without" is matter; life involves the coordination but not the violation of physico-chemical forces.

To be sure, Teilhard agrees with Lamarck that the *interior life* of organisms contributed to evolutionary change. But this thesis does not depend on the discredited Lamarckian theory that characteristics acquired during a creature's lifetime can be inherited by its descendants. A number of prominent biologists who accept a basically Darwinian framework assign a major role in evolution to an organism's mentality and initiative (in selecting its own environment, in the phenomenon of "genetic assimilation," etc.). One would hardly find such distinguished scientists as Julian Huxley, C. H. Waddington and Theodosius Dobzhansky endorsing *The Phenomenon of Man* if it were incompatible with present-day biological science.

Teilhard as Poet and Mystic

But if that book does not *contravene* science, it surely goes *beyond* science even as most broadly defined. *The Phenomenon of Man* often uses scientific terms metaphorically (e.g., "radial energy," "psychic temperature"). It treats vague analogies as if they were proofs from which conclusions follow "inevitably," "inescapably" and "infallibly." It would have been helpful if Teilhard had more clearly differentiated between accepted scientific data and speculative philosophical proposals. He presents the most tenuous extrapolations from debatable premises as if they were as certain as facts about the skull of Peking Man. Thus his statement in the preface that *The Phenomenon of Man* should be read "purely and simply as a scientific treatise" seems quite misleading. These features have led the more intemperate critics (e.g., Medawar) to call the volume "nonsense" and the more restrained (e.g., Simpson) to label it "poetry."

Now there is indeed something of the poet in Teilhard's vision of a unified cosmic process. The vivid imagery of his evolutionary epic is powerfully evocative. His own sense of the grandeur of an ascending and interdependent world, his lyric love of nature and ecstatic affirmation of life call forth similar reactions in the reader. From *The Divine Milieu* and *Hymn of the Universe* one might conclude that Teilhard was primarily a mystic, a modern St. Francis, moved by the experience of God's presence in nature. Perhaps it was his profound life of prayer, more than his work as a scientist, that brought him to an intuitive vision of a world unified by God. Or perhaps we should call the *Phenomenon* a modern myth. Men in all ages have celebrated life through dramatic images and articulated their responses to the world symbolically through myths giving unity to their cosmos. Does not evolution simply provide the setting and imagery for Teilhard's poetic, mystical or mythical response?

Teilhard as Natural Theologian

Though it includes much scientific information, I cannot accept the *Phenomenon* as "straight science"; but neither can I dismiss it as "mere poetry," though its mode of expression is often poetic. Does it then present a new form of *natural theology* in which the directionality of evolution is taken as evidence for the existence of God? The classic "argument from design" assumed a static universe with fixed species created in their present forms, and concluded that there must have been an Intelligent Designer. The post-Darwinian version discerns design not in specific organisms but in the conditions and laws through which the evolution of higher forms could occur in a dynamic universe. Design is built into the whole law-abiding process by which life and mind were brought into being. Teilhard defends not divine intervention at special points but "a creation of evolutionary type (*God making things make themselves*)." Purpose, he finds, is expressed in the operation of the natural causes which produced directionality, not in the suspension of these causes. Much of Teilhard's appeal in a day of widespread anxiety and despair lies in his message of hope, a hope seemingly derived by projecting into the future the long ascent of the past.

Teilhard himself evidently considered the *Phenomenon* as an apologia aimed at the unbeliever; for in its pages he avoids reference to Christianity, except in a few footnotes and an epilogue. Many of his theological interpreters (e.g., Henri de Lubac, Olivier Rabut) classify the volume as in the tradition of natural theology, which has always had a respected place in Roman Catholicism as a preamble to revealed theology. Yet several questions might be raised about this way of reading it: (1) Is the argument from design in this new version as convincing as Teilhard claims? (2) Does this approach provide any rationale for the interaction of scientific and religious ideas which characterizes Teilhard's thought? I would submit that his ideas are deeply informed by the Christian tradition even when the latter is not explicitly mentioned. He has given us a genuine *synthesis* of scientific and religious insights, rather than an inference from science alone. In that synthesis his metaphysics plays a crucial part.

Teilhard as Process Philosopher

Teilhard was not trained in philosophy as he was in science and to some extent in theology. Nevertheless his *process metaphysics*, though not formally developed, seems to have been the "middle term" through which his evolutionary outlook influenced his theology and vice versa. Where *being* and *substance* were scholastic philosophy's basic categories, *becoming* and *process* are Teilhard's. Time, change and interaction are constitutive of reality. Ours is a world in flux, a network of interacting influences spread through time and space. Teilhard's metaphysics strikingly resembles that of the philosopher Alfred North Whitehead—in part, no doubt, because of their common indebtedness to evolutionary thought in general and to Henri Bergson in particular. Both men stress the continuity of evolutionary history and of the levels of life today. The capacities of higher organisms were present in rudimentary form in the lower. There are no sharp lines of demarcation between the "living" and the "nonliving," or between "mental" and "nonmental" life. Yet there were "thresholds" or "critical points" which mark new levels of organization such as the advent of reflective thought.

Teilhard, like Whitehead, pictures every entity as a center of spontaneity and responsiveness. Of course neither thinker imputes to simpler organisms any self-consciousness or reflection, but only an incipient *"within,"* an elementary beginning of perception and anticipation "in extremely attenuated versions." Both however consider man's consciousness a valuable clue to the interpretation of the world because (1) it is the only aspect of reality of which we have direct awareness; (2) it is a product of the evolutionary process and therefore indicative of the potentialities of lower forms; and (3) there are no sharp lines between levels of reality, which is *one continuous process.* Man's experience is an extreme instance of an event in nature, and hence exhibits the generic features of all experience. In any case, "mind" and "matter" are not two separate substances but two ways of regarding a single complex entity with various levels of organization. This view is consistent with the biblical outlook concerning the unity of man as a total being and the importance of man in the universe.

Again, Teilhard's insistence on the evolutionary and historical character of reality is in accord with the Bible's affirmative attitude toward *time* and *history.* Greek thought had been obsessed with the timeless and had disparaged temporality and change as hallmarks of an inferior realm; truth was outside time, a realm of eternal forms and unchanging essences. Hebrew thought, by contrast, looked on history as the sphere of God's redemptive purposes, and concerned itself with truth-in-action. Scholastic thought tried to combine these two traditions but tended to exalt static over dynamic categories. Now Teilhard's evolutionary perspective made him more sensitive to the Hebrew attitude toward temporality. Hence he portrayed not Aristotle's Unmoved Mover but the Bible's Living God, involved in time and participating in a continuing creation.

Teilhard as Christian Theologian

Teilhard's process metaphysics thus influenced his theology, especially his rendering of the doctrines of *creation, redemption* and *eschatology*. These themes are implicit in the *Phenomenon* and explicit in *The Divine Milieu* and in some of his shorter essays which will soon be published in French (discussions of them in English are available in volumes by de Lubac, Mooney, North and Smulders). Teilhard urges us to think of creation "not as an instantaneous act, but in the manner of a process or synthesizing action. . . . Its act is a great continuous movement spread out over the totality of time. It is still going on." That is to say, we are part of an embryonic cosmos still in birth. Our understanding of God's relation to the world must take into account our knowledge of the temporal character of that world. Divine creativity is not arbitrary but has a definite structure, "the unification of the multiple" and "the creative transformation of earlier forms."

His evolutionary outlook leads Teilhard to declare *the unity of creation and redemption.* In his view the purpose of the incarnation is less the "remedial" work of making satisfaction for man's sin than the "constructive" work of uniting all reality and bringing it to fulfillment in God. Grace is not primarily an antidote for moral evil but a creative force at work throughout the world and human life. Where Western tradition has stressed the juridical and moral functions of Christ, Teilhard stresses his cosmic and ontological significance. Christ is not a foreign intruder sent arbitrarily to an alien realm to rescue individuals from it. He is the world's true fulfillment, integrally related to whatever is creative in the world. Redemption is the continuation of creation and vice versa. Here are ideas reminiscent of the Greek Fathers' "Universal Lord," John's "Logos" and Paul's "Christ in whom all things cohere." Teilhard sets forth a strong *theology of the secular*, affirming the positive potentialities of the world and rejecting any dualism which considers matter inherently evil. If God is involved in the world—in continuous creation and in the person of Christ—the Christian life must likewise entail involvement in the world. In this appreciation of the values in secularity Teilhard is not unlike Bonhoeffer, Cox and other exponents of "worldly Christianity."

In terms similar to Whitehead's, Teilhard portrays a *reciprocal interaction* between God and the world. The universe is not "useless" and "superfluous" to God, nor is he "indifferent" to it. "Truly it is not the notion of the contingency of the created but the sense of the mutual completion of God and the world which makes Christianity live." Teilhard argues that when men believed the world was created instantaneously it was difficult to reconcile the *presence of evil* with the goodness and power of God; but in an evolutionary creation God is exonerated because evil is an inevitable by-product. "There can be no order in process of formation that does not at all its stages involve disorder." The pain of failure and death are structural concomitants of evolutionary growth. Suffering is "the consequence and price of a labor of development."

The orthodoxy of some of Teilhard's teachings has been questioned by his more conservative theological critics. The accusation of pantheism seems unfounded, since he explicitly defends God's transcendence even if he puts the emphasis on immanence. Like the Christian mystics, he speaks of personal union with God rather than of absorption of the individual in an impersonal All. A more serious deficiency may be present in his treatment of sin as simply one form of inescapable evil in the world; he tends to neglect the moral dimensions of individual freedom and divine forgiveness. But there can be no question about his personal devotion to Christ and the Roman Catholic Church—to which he remained loyal despite his distress at being forbidden to publish his manuscripts. Today, a dozen years after his death and two years after the Vatican Council, there are signs of new openness to many of his ideas among Catholics, not only in northern Europe but in America. His writings are also being widely read and appreciated in Protestant circles, and seminars devoted to them have been introduced in a number of leading theological schools.

Teilhard as Prophet of the Future

Consider finally Teilhard's conclusions as he turns from the past to the future of a world still in birth. In the later chapters of the *Phenomenon*, in *The Future of Man* and in *Man's Place in Nature*, he extrapolates the apparent direction of past evolution to a future global convergence of mankind into an interthinking fabric of humanity, a collectivity of consciousness ("the Noosphere"). Believing that the universe is "personalizing" and "individuating," he is confident that this new "social organism" will be informed by freedom and diversity rather than totalitarian uniformity. The bond uniting the new humanity will be love. Perhaps Teilhard gives too little attention to the differences between biological and cultural evolution, and extrapolates too readily from one to the other. He seems to underestimate the tragic and ambiguous character of human history. True, he acknowledges that, with the advent of reflective thought, man—who is "evolution conscious of itself"—chooses his own destiny and now has the power to destroy himself. Nevertheless he is convinced that the cosmic process, having gone so far as it has, will inevitably progress further. One wonders whether this assurance about the future did not derive as much from his Christian faith as from his empirical study of man.

The Teilhardian view of *the final fulfillment* combines an evolutionary optimism with a Christian eschatology in which the activity of man and the world contribute to the actualization of the Kingdom. The maturation of man is "a condition (not indeed sufficient and determinative but necessary) for the Parousia of Christ." Man and nature collaborate with God in bringing the cosmos to completion; evolutionary development and human endeavor cooperate with the unifying and creative divine action. Salvation is not an escape from the world but its completion and sanctification. Yet the ending is not merely the intrinsic climax of a process ascending "on its own" without God. For God is at work throughout history, and the consummation of history is a gift of his grace. This is neither a purely "natural ascent" nor an arbitrary "supernatural finale" unrelated to what went before; the action is both "natural" and "supernatural" throughout, until the ultimate consummation which is the culmination of Teilhard's cosmic vision.

Teilhard's Synthesis of Science and Religion

Thus Teilhard's writings can profitably be read in a variety of ways: as science, as poetry, as natural theology, as process philosophy, and as Christian theology. Many interpreters have sharply contrasted his various works, classifying the *Phenomenon*, for instance, as natural theology and *The Divine Milieu* as Christian theology. I have suggested, however, that there is unity in his thought and that both evolutionary and biblical assumptions influenced all his writing, though obviously in varying degrees. The role of Teilhard's process metaphysics as a "middle term" here has often been overlooked. Whether he intended to or not, he deals with questions that have traditionally been the province of metaphysics: mind and matter, purpose and mechanism, the relationship between nature, man and God. It is precisely his temporalistic metaphysics that enables him to develop a process theology emphasizing such genuinely biblical themes as the importance of time and history, affirmation of "secular" life, the unity of man as a total being, belief in a living God involved in the world, and the cosmic significance of Christ. As I see it, Teilhard's most original work is his exploration of the nature of man and the meaning of creation, redemption and eschatology in an evolving world.

Any such synthesis of scientific and religious insights will encounter a number of objections. It may be claimed that *theology* is revealed, accepted on faith, immune to any influence from science. Yet many Protestant and Catholic writers today hold that theology is not itself revealed, that rather theology is the interpretation of revelatory events by means of human categories of thought. In particular, it is often recognized that one's view of God's relation to the world cannot ignore the character of the world. Moreover, metaphysical assumptions are seen to be inescapable in the theologian's work. The status of temporality in Teilhard's process metaphysics, and the preoccupation with the history of the world evident in his works, may be peculiarly compatible with the Bible's predominantly historical categories. Again, it may be objected that *metaphysics* is a secular exercise of reason alone. But surely philosophy is historically conditioned and in Western culture has often been profoundly affected by the biblical tradition. Adepts of *lin-

guistic philosophy may insist that science and religion are contrasting languages serving very different functions in human life. Yet there are signs that the cognitive functions of religious language are being taken more seriously by philosophers; problems once dismissed as "metaphysical" are again being discussed.

In a time when many men have abandoned the quest for synthesis, Teilhard's attempt, even where it is only partly successful, is a standing criticism of our complacency in settling so readily for a plurality of totally unrelated languages. He refused to assign ideas to watertight compartments. Perhaps our generation should not expect to reach any grand all-inclusive synthesis; perhaps we shall have to accept tentative and limited analyses, using a variety of models under diverse circumstances. But Teilhard's conviction of the coherence of truth and the unity of the universe can inspire our hope of compassing even so modest a goal as honest dialogue between the disciplines. Though his most impressive gifts were those of personal witness and profound spirituality rather than intellectual precision or philosophical abstraction, the importance of his ideas should not be minimized.

Teilhard himself never looked on his formulations as a closed and final system. He wrote near the end of the *Phenomenon*, "It is up to others to try to do better." His thought is suggestive but incomplete. He was no Aquinas articulating a systematic *Summa* that could stand for centuries and serve to integrate a whole cultural epoch. Though Teilhard shared Aquinas' breadth of outlook and dedication to synthesis, his ideas were at best exploratory. As it stands his work is subject to criticism by the standards of each of the disciplines. Even so, it will be challenge and stimulus to thinkers in many fields. And in a day of specialization and fragmentation, his concern for the totality of man and his vision of a unified world may prove his most enduring contribution.

EVOLUTION: IMPLICATIONS FOR RELIGION

The problem of human evolution is far wider than genetics or biology, or than science as a whole.

THEODOSIUS DOBZHANSKY

Neither Dante nor his contemporaries, back in the 13th century, had the slightest doubt that the earth was made expressly and specifically for man—for his enjoyment and use and for his chastisement. They believed too that the whole universe was quite recent, only some 5,000 years old, and they did not expect it to endure very long; they saw its end or radical transformation as imminent. Anyone who felt that these views were puzzling or mysterious had a safe way to clarify them: *nisi crederitis non intelligetis*—you will not understand unless you believe, as St. Augustine repeated again and again.

Copernicus, and soon after him Kepler and Galileo, questioned certain details in the accepted scheme of things. The earth, they said, is not the center of the universe but only one of the planets revolving around the sun. The celebrated trial and recantation of Galileo followed. The view he advanced is not even yet universally accepted. As reported in the *New York Times*, Sheik Abdel Aziz bin Baz, vice president of the Islamic University of Medina, wrote in 1966:

. . . the Holy Koran, the Prophet's teachings, the majority of Islamic scientists, and the actual facts all prove

Dr. Dobzhansky is professor of zoology at Rockefeller University, New York City.

that the sun is running in its orbit, . . . and that the earth is fixed and stable, spread out by God for his mankind . . . Anyone who professed otherwise would utter . . . a charge of falsehood toward God, the Koran, and the Prophet.

Newton went much farther than Copernicus. He declared that the universe is an immense machine. It operates according to sublimely precise and immutable laws established by God, but it is a machine nevertheless. The earth is a mere speck in the vastness of cosmic space. Newton himself was a student of the Apocalypse as well as of cosmology. To many, however, the Newtonian universe seemed a cold and soulless place. Pascal expressed his loneliness poignantly: "The eternal silence of these infinite spaces frightens me"—a plaint echoed today. For instance, Jacques Barzun writes that "when techne assails the senses and science dominates the mind," "something pervasive that makes the difference, not between civilized man and the savage, not between man and the animals, but between man and the robot, grows numb, ossifies, falls away like black mortified flesh."

Post-Darwinian Disillusionment

A century and a half later Darwin, as some charge, completed the nefarious process of grinding to dust man's image. Darwin held that, far from being the center of the universe, man is a newcomer even on this second-rate planet in a mediocre solar system. Man is a descendant of apelike animals; and he arose owing to the operation of mechanical causes which act equally on man, on dumb animals, on plants and even on microbes. Reactions to this disillusionment were diverse. Some fought a losing but not yet ended battle against evolutionism. Others, accepting it, have been led to a deeply pessimistic and sometimes cynical world view which holds that the universe has neither sense nor purpose. Thus Julian Huxley announces triumphantly that "man is alone" and can have only a "religion without revelation." Raymond S. Nogar, a theologian as well as a biologist, in his book *The Lord of the Absurd* finds obvious and painful "the disorder, the waste, the hectic disorganization of the fragments of the universe of reality." It is, he says, "a point of realism that the universe of matter, of man and divine influence have been shattered and fragmented."

True, one has to be purblind not to notice the disorder, the waste, the fragmentation, pain and evil. But there is a fundamental difference between Newton's universe and Darwin's. The one was serenely unchanging; in the other change is of the essence. The central affirmation of evolution is that what we see here and now is different from what was and from what will be. And, most important, while the past cannot be changed, the future may conceivably be influenced and even planned in accord with what man regards as good and desirable. Creation is not an act but a process; it did not happen five or six thousand years ago but is going on before our eyes. Man is not compelled to be a mere spectator; he may become an assistant, a collaborator, a partner in the process of creation.

Here lies the hopeful aspect of evolutionism—a hopefulness that is not mere wishful thinking but has a basis in what man has discovered. The cosmic, inorganic, inanimate evolution led to the origin, some 2 billion years ago, of a remarkable process, called life, on at least one of the countless planets in the cosmos. Life has developed through processes (ably surveyed by William T. Keeton in a previous article in this book) that are neither economical nor very orderly. They are undirected, blind, and consequently, in our estimation, pretty wasteful and extravagant. But they are neither absurd nor evil. Among the millions of species that biological evolution has produced, there is one, Man, which has discovered that it s a product of evolution. Moreover, members of this pecies have developed some quite unique qualities; they an distinguish order from disorder, economy from waste, indness from cruelty, good from evil, what is from what ught to be. Thus a third kind of evolution has become uperimposed on the other two—the human, or cultural, nto the biological and the cosmic. (See "Cultural Evolution Today," by Julian H. Steward.)

Grounds for Optimism?

But what are the grounds for an evolutionary optimism? What basis do we have for expecting that the evolving world and evolving man will become any better in the future than they are today? Moreover, if he betterment is foreordained, will come regardless of what we do or do not do, what possible meaning can our existence have? (See "Evolutionary Science and the Dilemma of Freedom and Determinism," by Langdon Gilkey.) Some evolutionary biologists have held that the entire evolutionary process is planned and predestined; that, though it has to pass through a series of stages— some of them unpleasant and harsh in human estimation —all will be sweetness and light in the end.

If such were the case, man could only wait patiently for nature to take its course. In biology there are (or were) theories—finalism, orthogenesis, aristogenesis, nomogenesis, etc.—which held that evolution is either guided by some supernatural agent or is merely the unwinding of an internal spring which brings about a sequence of inevitable events. Some theories of cultural evolution also postulated a kind of cultural orthogenesis (see Dr. Steward's article). I shall attempt to show that other directions of thought are more fruitful and satisfactory. Evolution predestined would be evolution devoid of any meaning that man could recognize as sacred and even as estimable.

Freedom and Predestination

Many modern cosmologists favor so-called "Big-Bang" theories of the origin of the universe; that is, the universe started in a stupendous explosion which "cooked" the atoms of chemical elements and set the galaxies flying apart in the expanding universe. Whether the "Big Bang" happened 5, 10 or 15 billion years ago hardly matters. In any case, it took a very, very long time to evolve a planet on which life could arise, and for life to evolve man. Suppose that, counting from now, it will take a much shorter time to reach the consummation of the evolutionary process in the cosmic Parousia or in Teilhard de Chardin's Point Omega. If all this was predestined and will inevitably occur, we face some very uncomfortable questions: Why such a gargantuan waste of time? Why all the false starts, the countless extinctions, the senseless deaths—why, indeed, death at all? If nothing really new happens or can happen, if all was settled from the start, could not Almighty God have brought about the final result without this unconscionable delay? The problem of predestination has been a stumbling block for every theodicy. Predestination on a scale of 10 billion-plus years is intolerable. If the process of creation by evolution was planned to take that much time to arrive at something predetermined and guaranteed at the start, it was outrageously ill planned.

It is within neither my competence nor my capacity to solve the freedom-predestination problem. I would like only to point out some evidence that the evolutionary process, on both the biological and human levels, has in it certain elements that counteract the determinism and suggest the beginnings of freedom.

Considered as a whole, biological evolution may be described as an adaptive response of living matter to the challenges of the environment. Philosophically, the crucial point is how these responses occur. They are not imposed by the environment acting upon the organisms as though it were inert matter (as neo-Lamarckians wrongly supposed). In reality, the responses to environmental challenges are mediated by natural selection. A response is not guaranteed; it may or may not occur. A living species can respond only when its populations contain the appropriate genetic variants, which have arisen by mutation. In the absence of such variants no adaptive response takes place. Moreover, even on the simplest level—e.g., the adaptation of certain microorganisms to the presence of antibodies in the nutrient medium—the same challenge may be answered in more than one way; for these organisms have two or several gene loci, mutational changes in any one of which may confer a resistance to the same antibiotic, or an ability to utilize some new substance as food. Consequently, antibiotic-resistant strains of the same species need not be identical.

Nature's Creative Experiments

The indeterminacy increases as one passes to higher organisms and more complex changes. Adaptive genetic changes often involve building harmonious systems of many genes. My favorite example is desert plants. All of them must be adapted to the same environmental challenge—dryness and the danger of desiccation; yet they respond in a variety of ways. Cacti and some milkweeds have replaced leaves with spines and have transformed their stems into barrels filled with moisture but carrying chlorophyll in their outer tissues. The creosote bush and many other shrubs have leaves protectively covered with a resinous secretion or a thick coat of hair. Most numerous of desert plants are the annuals which grow, blossom, and ripen their seed when and if water happens to be plentiful. Some of them take no provision for the conservation of water but compress their life cycles into the shortest possible time, remaining dormant during the dry season. So far as we can judge, all these strategies are equally successful, and there is no way of telling why the evolutionary process has taken any one of these courses in preference to the others. Any naturalist will be able to give other examples of the variety of responses to similar environmental challenges.

I am not suggesting that biological species have freedom to choose the direction of their evolution. Freedom of choice in the human sense is certainly not a factor in evolution—except, of course, in the evolution of man. However, one of the most impressive biological phenomena is the diversity of living beings. At least 2 million species are now living, and probably several times that many existed in the past and became extinct. And within each species—at least those that reproduce sexually—every individual has a genetic endowment different from that of any other individual. Teilhard de Chardin said that life is trying out everything in order to discover everything. "Everything" is an overstatement: Teilhard was unaware of the fact that the numbers of potentially possible genetic endowments far exceed the numbers that can be realized. On the most conservative estimates of the numbers of genes and their possible changes, the potential genotypes are vastly more numerous than the atoms and the sub-atomic particles in the universe. Indeed, in a sense the genetic mechanisms which create ever new gene constellations are far more powerful than they need be in this small universe. What these mechanisms do accomplish is however quite remarkable. Not only every living species but every individual is nature's creative experiment, trying out different ways of life in different environments. It is a *creative* experiment in the same sense that a poem is the poet's and a painting the painter's creative experiment. Every gene constellation never existed before and will not be repeated, and it is tested for its coherence and "value" to remain alive.

Biological evolution is, then, a gigantic trial-and-error operation. Its outcome evidently does not fit any reasonable definition of freedom in the human sense. There is however in the course of the evolution a growth of a kind of unconstraint which makes the evolutionary process unpredictable save for short time intervals, and even then only under exceptionally favorable circumstances. The source of this indeterminacy is that there are many ways of becoming adapted to, and remaining alive in, the environments which the surface of our planet offers. This is one of the reasons why many biologists, including this writer, are skeptical about the presence of "hominoids" on planets other than our own. Even if some kind of life has arisen in many places in the universe, it is utterly unlikely that its evolution has followed a course even remotely similar to that followed on earth.

A Legitimate Anthropocentricity

To say that the origin of man has been the paramount achievement of the organic evolution is a legitimate anthropocentricity, though it is going too far to suppose (as some writers have done) that the whole organic evolution was designed for the sole purpose of bringing man into being. Darwin titled one of his books *The Descent of Man*. "The *Ascent* of Man" would have been more appropriate; for man has indeed ascended to a level above the animal. This view has been challenged by the statement that to a fish the highest achievement of evolution would be a fish; to which G. G. Simpson rightly answers: "I suspect that the fish's reaction would be, instead, to marvel that there are men who question the fact that man is the highest animal. . . . the 'fish' that made such judgment would have to be a man!"

I am certainly not contending that evolution was, or is beginning to be, acausal. If we had complete knowledge of all the causes operating, then, theoretically, all evolution would be predictable. The key words in that sentence are "complete knowledge." Remember Laplace's celebrated dictum: that if "all the forces acting in nature at a given instant, as well as the momentary positions of all things in the Universe" were known, then an intellect "sufficiently powerful to subject all data to analysis" could with certainty predict all future and retrodict all past events. According to Ernest Nagel, however, Laplace was "guilty of a serious *non sequitur*," because "such claims would be warranted only if, in addition to knowing these things, Laplace's divine intelligence would be able to analyze all traits of physical objects whatsoever . . . as definable in terms of the variables that constitute the mechanical state of a system. However, mechanics does not rest on the assumption that such an analysis is in fact possible."

Evolutionary Transcendences

Causality and freedom must not be regarded as incompatible alternatives. Let us consider again, from this point of view, the evolutionary history of the universe. The two outstanding events or critical turning points were the origin of life and the origin of man. These ushered in novel systems of causality: the biological and the cultural—a statement that in no sense implies anything even remotely resembling a vital force or a supernatural soul suddenly appearing on the stage. Since, as we hold, biological phenomena are patterns of physical and chemical components, reduction of biological processes to the processes of chemistry and physics is, at least in principle, possible. Human affairs are patterns of reactions and interactions of the individuals of one peculiar biological species, *Homo sapiens*. What, then, makes biological and social sciences different from each other and from the physical sciences? It is simply that to understand life and men we must study the biological and sociological patterns as well as their components. A mosaic picture consists of stones of various colors, but what makes it a picture is the pattern in which the stones are set; otherwise we have a pile of stones.

It is difficult to find a word to characterize the major turning points of evolution. With the appearance of life, and again with the appearance of man, something quite novel entered the world. "Emergence" would be appropriate were it not for the fact that this word was utilized for a theory of "emergent evolution" (a theory that now has very few followers since it is wrong and misleading). In a book recently published (*The Biology of Ultimate Concern*) I have called these turning points "evolutionary transcendences"—a term not connected with any kind of philosophical transcendentalism or with the biological vitalism that E. W. Sinnott has recently attempted to resuscitate in a series of books. Sinnott has not presented any new arguments in favor of vitalism. In the main he repeats those set forth almost half a century ago by H. Driesch, and rightly rejected by an overwhelming majority of biologists. Majorities are, certainly, not always right, but I fail to see any cogency or usefulness in Sinnott's vitalism, either scientifically or philosophically. This vitalism fails to take evolution seriously. To hold that complex organs, or whole organisms, arise by a lucky combination of random changes is certainly too far-fetched to be credible. Evolution simply does not happen in this way. Organs and organisms arose by 2 billion years of natural selection; they were always adapted to live in some environment; and changes were added and superadded gradually, when such changes made even slight improvements in the functioning of existing systems.

What, then, is evolutionary transcendence? The phenomena of life outstrip, overpass, rise above the limits of the chemical and physical processes in inorganic nature, without being contrary to or incompatible or unconnected with those processes. Humanity transcends animality; man is an animal, but he is also much more than an animal. Anyone who doubts this should do what K. Lorenz suggests: that he "try—only in imagination, of course—to kill in succession a lettuce, a fly, a frog, a guinea pig, a cat, a dog, and finally a chimpanzee." Lorenz adds: "To any man who finds it equally easy to chop up a live dog and live lettuce I would recommend suicide!"

The Uniqueness of Man

Transcendence is an elaboration of the novel patterns of phenomena of underlying levels, not an addition of novel immanent qualities. Life is a novel pattern of chemical and physical phenomena, and man is a novel pattern of biological, hence of chemical and physical, components. Teilhard predicted new transcendences to come. Human evolution will transcend itself in what he called megasynthesis and finally in Point Omega (his symbol for God). Teilhard extrapolates from what did happen in evolution to what he thinks will happen. This is the realm of prophecy rather than science; but if I understand him aright, he expects the hoped-for transcendences to arise through novel patternings of the existing evolutionary processes and components. Thus what Teilhard created is an evolutionary theodicy. Its attractiveness—to me at least—lies in that it postulates the growth of freedom as the inner meaning of the history of the cosmos.

Teilhard describes the novelty of man as follows: "The animal certainly knows. Yet it does not know that it knows. . . . Compared to animals, since we reflect, we are not only different but unlike. This is not simply a quantitative change but a change of nature, resulting from a change of state." Are these words anything more than a biologist's paraphrase of the parable of the Forbidden Fruit? Is man more or less happy than an animal? We do not know for sure; but we suspect that this is a meaningless question. In any case the evolutionary transcendence is irreversible. Man is burdened with self-awareness and death-awareness. All living beings die, but man alone knows that his death is inevitable. Is this knowledge the source, or merely one of the sources, of man's ultimate concern?

To repeat: adaptive response to environmental challenges is the mainspring of biological evolutionary change —a statement that applies also to the evolutionary transcendence in man's origin from his prehuman ancestors. The stages of man's ascent have been reviewed by Dr. Steward in his article in this series. Man is not only a tool user but also a tool maker; he is capable of symbolic and abstract thought; he communicates by means of symbolic language; he has created culture, which is transmitted not by genes but by teaching and learning. By any reasonable criteria man is the most successful biological species in existence. He adapts his environments to his genes more frequently and efficiently than his genes to his environments. His death-awareness and self-awareness may be only by-products of the biological adaptive change in our ancestors. Yet they became the most distinctive characteristics of our kind. They make up what some philosophers and theologians have called the *humanum*.

Facing the Future

Man not only can foresee but can plan a future. As his knowledge increases, so does his ability to realize his plans. Knowledge is power, increasing knowledge is increasing power. But man's power has a peculiar limitation. More than any animal, man faces the problem of choosing from among the possible plans those to be executed and those to be left in abeyance. The ability to choose brings responsibility. And nowhere are the possible consequences of choice more portentous than in changing the direction of the evolution of our species. No longer is man forced to accept his evolution as imposed upon him by natural causes beyond his understanding and control. He is becoming able to govern his evolution. The gravity of the responsibility thus entailed is evident. Man's "nature" is surely by far his most valuable possession. In a brilliant article in this book ("What Man Can Make of Man"), Karl H. Hertz analyzes the problem concisely yet thoroughly. I can only say that I agree with him on all major points.

In Dr. Hertz's article I count 33 sentences ending in question marks. This is not destructive skepticism but much needed caution. Too many inventors of eugenical utopias seem to feel no need of question marks at all. Indeed, one shudders at their smug assurance that they know not only precisely what the ideal man must be but even how to get the ideal man by their favorite breeding techniques. This is not to deny that the known breeding techniques are powerful and, if consistently and universally applied, would in a dozen or so generations (which in man means about three centuries) change human "nature" appreciably. One recalls a proposal urged particularly by the eminent biologist H. J. Muller and Sir Julian Huxley: to institute sperm banks and mass artificial insemination of women, whose husbands, presumably, will not consider their own genes as worth passing on. As Dr. Hertz points out, the problem involved here is sociological and even political, not only biological. Indeed the more dependable and the more widely applied the breeding technique employed, the more certainly will politicians of all stripes try to control its goals and its uses. To ignore these issues is the height of irresponsibility. As another eminent biologist—G. W. Beadle—puts it: man knows enough but is not yet wise enough to make Man.

The difficulty of instituting a program of human breeding does not lie in today's biological technologies; what insufficiencies it has could be remedied with relative ease. The real difficulty is the lack of certainty—not to speak of the lack of general agreement—as to the goals which human evolution should aim at. Does this mean that man must give up hope of ever controlling his own evolution? That decision may well prove suicidal in the long run. What then? I believe that what is needed is a frank recognition that the problem of human evolution is far wider than genetics or biology, or than science as a whole.

The universe is evolving, and man is a part of the cosmic process. But he need not be a passive spectator. He may become an increasingly active participant in the process of creation. Here is the greatest challenge ever put to human thought and human culture—the ultimate challenge, and a part of the ultimate concern. In other words, it is a religious challenge. For, religion, as Tillich said, "is the meaning-giving substance of culture, and culture is the totality of forms in which the basic concern of religion expresses itself." Or: "Religion is the substance of culture, culture is the form of religion." So it may be that, after all, we have to agree with St. Augustine: *Nisi credideritis non intelligetis.*

EVOLUTION AND BEING FAITHFUL

*It is wrong to assume that Christian concepts will be-
come meaningful again only when incorporated into ever
larger intellectual syntheses.*

PAUL L. HOLMER

For some people a scientific hypothesis is either an
affirmative or a negative answer to religious inquiry.
Some of the writers in this series have frankly declared
for science as a criterion. Others, more mildly, have
averred that the church and Christians must come to
terms with science, especially evolution, in order to pros-
per. I shall argue that, granted its importance in the intellectual community, so far as religion is concerned the
principle of evolution is still largely irrelevant and ex-
traneous.

This is not to say that evolution is false. On the contrary, as William Keeton noted in his article introducing
this book ("Evolution: Basic to Biology"), evolutionary
theory is no longer a hypothesis seeking confirmation; it
has been attested by skilled research and reflection over
the past century and has virtually become a fundamental
principle in modern biology. The mass of empirical detail said to be illuminated by that principle, while allowing for disagreements and mistaken inferences, no longer
permits a significantly independent judgment in biology.
So I propose no novel ratifications and certainly no
vetoes, divine or otherwise. Indeed, I confess to deep

Dr. Holmer is professor of theology at Yale University divinity
school.

appreciation of the talents and labors that have made evolution a prevailing scientific conclusion in our time.

Scientists as Metaphysicians

My interest lies elsewhere. I am concerned with matters which might be called—in a somewhat limited sense —philosophical and theological. Also, I am perplexed by an attitude, evidenced more than once in this series, which contends that the church and its theologians have considerable accommodating to do with respect to the intellectual world. Why not the U.S. Senate, labor unions and teachers of music as well? Besides, I must admit that I am absolutely blind to a God who, supposedly, is evident in electrons but not in atoms, in organismic but not in mechanical concepts. Nor can I see evidence of God in religious enthusiasm which waxes with invariant species but wanes with their mutability, or find consolation in the principle of complementarity but not in that of relativity. Knowledge is a power, of course, and with all the potentialities available in DNA and command of the genetic code, we do have something to worry about. For who shall be the designer and what shall be designed? But important as this issue is, I wish to deal with another one altogether.

It cannot be denied that the processes of life, when studied in detail and formulated with appropriate conceptual tools, evoke great eagerness and enthusiasm in even the most steely of observers. Sometimes that eagerness is (to quote William James) "more knit up with the motor activities, sometimes with the perceptions, sometimes with the imagination, sometimes with reflective thought." But, James adds, "wherever it is found, there is the zest, tingle, the excitement of reality." Some writers on evolution and genetics convey this eagerness and excitement, thus making delightful what otherwise might be rather dull reading. We ought indeed to be grateful that there are eminent scientists—Theodosius Dobzhansky, Alister Hardy, George G. Simpson, Julian Huxley to name a few—who can convey this enthusiasm. But often something else slips into their writings. For instance Dobzhansky's "implications" are frequently only "suggestions." And in their eagerness to speak meaningfully and in the large, such writers as Pierre Teilhard de Chardin, Herbert H. Ross, Pierre Lecomte du Noüy, Edmund W. Sinnott (note especially Sinnott's *The Biology of the Spirit*, 1955), tend to malform scientific and biological concepts. Thus Teilhard speaks of "evolutionary gravity" as pulling matter into organization. The birth of the universe he calls "cosmogenesis" and the appearance of life "biogenesis." His "anthropogenesis" brings us man. Then comes "Christogenesis"—eventual man, "Christified" and supernaturalized. So evolution, even as an "inner urge," pulls matter through stages of development—from atoms to molecules, proteins and viruses, to cells, animals and men, then to social, economic and religious unification.

The other authors I have mentioned give us almost paradigmatic instances of kinds of metaphysics, which they link both to evolutionary biology and to religio-philosophical views. Lecomte expounds "telefinalism": God likened to a will that chooses to make things evolve. Professor Ross proposes (in *A Synthesis of Evolutionary Theory*, 1962) a variant on materialism slightly different from Lecomte's. Professor Sinnott, whose biological competence is patent, urges that both body and mind are "derived from something deeper than either"—something which, it turns out, is God.

It is the logic of this kind of argument that concerns me. There are scientists who, not content with scientific inquiry, must postulate a new world view, touch on ultimate concerns and bring God onto the scene. Many people today seem to hunger for an assurance that every scientific advance necessitates a complete reversal of fundamental ethical and religious convictions. So the argument moves from scientific theory, which looks to be so well established and substantial, to ultimate matters, regarding which our convictions do not seem too well established and are far from substantial. God, the future, good and evil—these beckon us in the quest for new realities.

I shall limit my comments to pointing out the logical pitfalls in two extremes. So far as morals and faith are concerned, we ought to be neither encouraged nor discouraged by evolution, for morals and faith have their own foundation. The flourishing business of supplying scientific crutches for their support does injustice to science and scientists on the one hand and to the springs of morals and faith on the other.

A Confusion of Concepts

Religious concepts such as God, grace, forgiveness, sin and love have a distinctive source and a distinctive power. It may be that that power is diminished today and that other concepts—scientific and political—have much more power. But the distinctiveness remains. The qualitative difference of religious from scientific or philosophical concepts is frequently glossed over when we attempt to articulate or defend religion either by seeking new supports for it in the newest scientific discovery or philosophical speculation, or, on a more practical level, by describing religion as an instrument of efficiency, as guaranteeing the successes we naturally desire. For these interpretations, while promising intellectual clarity and energy in the game of life, can also bring confusion to the very enterprise they seek to strengthen. Religious concepts have often become confused and generalized—sometimes by a too easy assimilation into the textures of ordinary discourse, sometimes by long academic flights that render them airborne and cut them off from all connection with everyday life.

The religious life profits greatly from criticism. Thus one of Augustine's important theological contributions is his correction of the tendency to use scriptural concepts to feed the enthusiasm for mysteries and cosmological speculation. On their part, Luther and Calvin restored scriptural concepts to a kind of plain use and sense, against the tendency to confine them to the realm of schools and scholars. And Wesley revivified those concepts after their genteel absorption by the English church. Religious concepts have no built-in safeguards, and they remain viable only so long as criticism keeps them in their proper place and deep devotion attests their worth.

It is difficult, however, to resist replacing everything old by something new. Because the intellectual life is so largely a matter of replacing one hypothesis with another, everything old looks vulnerable. Hence replacing a religious concept with a scientific one becomes plausible, not least when the latter is widely espoused. But the fact is that scientific concepts and most religious concepts lack the identity factor that would permit them to confirm, contradict or supplant each other. Besides, religious teachings are not hypotheses, nor are their components always a reflection of the age in which they were conceived; they are often part of that impressive residuum of human reflection that is not dated and is not obviously historical. The categories and concepts of that residuum are not conceived by specialists, not derived from the convulsive efforts of individual thinkers. Hence no history of thought describes their origin; it only gives an account of the permutations the concepts undergo and the difficulties of keeping intact the core of religion.

Surely it is a subtle confusion that leads men to trust science and distrust their eyes and ears. If eyes and ears tell us one thing about the world and science tells us another, does it follow that these senses are less reliable than science? It is common sense to acknowledge that we can control our lives to a large extent. However, as Langdon Gilkey has reminded us in this book ("Evolutionary Science and the Dilemma of Freedom and Determinism"), much of science seems to argue for determinism and even fatalism. Must we therefore reject common sense, ethical judgments, the notion of responsibility? Does science replace our everyday conviction in regard to these matters because it seems to do so in regard to other matters? This is precisely the point. Scientific concepts do not have such generality. Like that of other kinds of specialized discourse, their authority is strictly limited.

Radical Heterogeneity

Urgent as we may feel such considerations are, it behooves us not to generalize nor to be taken in by rhetorical figures and loose analogues. We must resist the pseudo-comforting view that science and religion are only different ways of knowing, or different languages about, the same reality. On the contrary, our common sense deals with needs different from those dealt with by special inquiries. Evolution and faith grow out of different needs, have different purposes, satisfy different requirements and embody different principles. The respective concepts are radically heterogeneous. That is why it is the better part of wisdom to live with the differences, rather than to cultivate the slenderest of analogues in search of new wisdom.

In the 19th century Claude Bernard, noting a tendency to pattern biology after physics and other inorganic sciences, argued that biology had its own special problems and points of view, and that it could employ the tools but not the concepts of other sciences. So, too, recent study of how scientific concepts work shows that the criterion of "verifiable prediction"—which is so generally accepted that it almost appears to be the mark of rationality—does not really apply to Darwin's theory of origination by variation and natural selection.* That part of Darwin's work has never been the subject of verified prediction. It does not follow, of course, that the theory is unscientific or merely speculative. The point is that the so-called general criterion is not that general—does not cover all the sciences. But for Christians who gobble up the crumbs that drop from the rich tables of science and trim the sails of their faith with every wind of philosophical doctrine, another admonition is in order: "Take courage, throw off your inhibitions—you have nothing to lose but your confusions!" Theology has ample ambiguities, irrelevancies, absurdities; it also has criteria, powers, principles, concepts by which it can be reanimated.

Generalization: Risky but Necessary

This is not to say that we should not generalize. Both evolutionary thought and Christian theology prompt generalizations as a matter of course. It is ridiculous to believe that either science or theology, research or faith can rest satisfied with a bare transcript of human experience. The impulse to generalize is ineradicable; it is simply part of what we mean by "thinking." Yet generalization carries all kinds of risks. There is a difference between a generalization which has only psychological justification and one which has the support of logic. In respect to logic, however, we must not be too restrictive, must not contend that the only logically warranted generalization is a logical deduction (of the kind we

* Cf. the interesting discussion by Bentley Glass, Stephen Toulmin and others in *Scientific Change*, edited by A. C. Crombie (Oxford University Press, New York, 1963), pp. 521–628.

encountered in beginning geometry and in the exercises of the logic textbook). We can generalize logically when, in virtue of how a concept in a given field actually functions, we have a warrant for extending the power of our language and learning.

Thus my criticism of theological uses of evolutionary thought, or of adaption of evolutionary ideas to matters of cosmology and morals, does not imply a demand for "just the facts." The solemn rhetoric we sometimes hear on behalf of plain facts is as restrictive of science as it is pernicious to theology and the life of faith. Of course, facts are facts, and no one can do without them. Nonetheless generalization, not recitation of facts, is the better part of learning as it is of theology. All have sinned, Paul says—thus generalizing the concept of sin. What Paul learned in the small cosmos of his own life gave him understanding of everyone else's. And when he and other Christians use the word "creation" to tell us that God made the world, they are making generalized use of "world," "made" and even "God." So generalization by itself is not necessarily the difficulty. It is *how* one generalizes, not *that* one generalizes, that makes for problems.

Generalization is subject to rules, but the rules are not themselves general; instead, they are perquisites of various kinds of learning and activity. For example, since in most consciously planned endeavors—scientific, religious, political—proposals promoting change are described and evaluated in terms of what does not change, one might be tempted to say that all such endeavors involve faith in the permanent. Yet the resemblance here is only a formal and empty one. The concept of "permanence" is clearly ambiguous, and the word betrays the user into unjustified generalizing. So, too, with "change." Hence the easy identification of the subject matter of religion with that of evolution by way of general words such as "history," "man" and "living things."

Christian theology, like the faith itself, is viable only if there is a matrix of reflection engendered by a man's experience of himself. But theology, again like faith, concerns not only that experience; it generalizes concerning earth, heaven, the past, the future—in fact, the Christian learns to refer everything to God. The sciences also have produced generalizations of remarkable scope and authenticity. Yet science and theology are not different languages expressive of the same reality, for neither theology nor science is "expressive" in the obvious sense of that term. The attempt to arrive at a generalization that bridges these two enterprises by virtue of a general theory of language—namely, that all language is expressive of a general theory of reality—is gratuitous. No inference can be drawn from science to theology or vice versa; and inferences and generalizations to a third and more inclusive reality or philosophical view have no authority other than their author's desire.

Nothing excites contemporary man quite so much as the promise of meaning. Almost any kind of wantonness, intellectual or behavioral, is condoned nowadays if it promises to lead toward "meaningfulness." But I speak here of more modest endeavors. Several authors in this series are striving to find a place for biology within a general *Weltanschauung*. In the vast evolutionary perspective, life arises from inorganic stuff, rational beings emerge, the lights of learning and culture begin to shine. But the pathology of the person also becomes manifest. Anxiety, guilt, hate and the fear of death are the somber accompaniments of self-awareness. From these, too, man's search for meaning takes its departure, and thus evolution and faith seem to be joined once more. The evolutionary process seems to require faith and religion, almost as the means to resolve the disabilities cast up by a wholly natural course of events. Simultaneously, faith—and all it engenders in a person's life-history—appears to have found its basis and explanation in the tissue of scientific fact.

Again, however, one must beware of eliding so many things in such commodious conceptual schemes. For it is simply not the case that explanations of the origin of life, of species, even of emotions and purposes, either destroy the differences between these and their antecedents, natural or otherwise, or enhance their meaning by identifying or ascribing a common origin to them. Salt does not lose its savor because we describe it chemically. The concept "salt" in everyday parlance is not made up of the subconcepts "sodium" and "chlorine," even though salt itself can be reduced to such components.

Contra Grand-Scale Syntheses

The notion that Christian and moral concepts need some kind of grounding in the natural order to enhance their meaning seems to me a radical misconception of those concepts. It is not true that a specific kind of continuity in the natural order affects the life of the human spirit. Evolution describes certain kinds of continuities, but the concepts by which those continuities are described are powerful only for the limited purpose they are designed for. The life of faith as molded in a Christian context does not take its point of departure here. The concepts used in delineating the pathology of the human spirit are specifically human in origin. Sin is not found in the brutes, and anyone who professes to find it there misunderstands the concept "sin." Forgiveness is not animal behavior; moral fault cannot be subsumed under biological categories; ancestral brutishness does not create the proclivity for irreligion. Good and evil are antitheses only for men who can choose (we cannot condemn animal behavior on moral grounds nor blame atoms for their course of motion); so, too, good and evil are not stages to be delineated in an evolutionary process.

What then about meaning? Admittedly, the concepts

of Christian theology have become meaningless for many people. But it is a mistake to assume that they will become meaningful again only when they are incorporated into ever larger and more comprehensive intellectual syntheses. Arnold Toynbee, Alfred North Whitehead and Pierre Teilhard de Chardin have devised concepts of far-reaching generality out of stimuli from history, mathematics and biology. But these sciences were only the point of departure, not the logical ground—and certainly not the evidence—for their syntheses. Conflicts in meanings have arisen in the past and will arise in the future. Both science and religion excite our passions and speed our reflection. But our tactic, in so far as it can be suggested in general terms, should be to note the differences and to shun the loose similarities. Of the exploitation of analogues we have too much already; of the discernment of the differences, altogether too little. Meaning resides in efficacious use. We find meaning in a religious life and in strenuous scientific endeavor, not in syntheses about them.

Making religion meaningful by subsuming it under evolutionary theory or, what is even more difficult, by trying to adapt religion to evolutionary views does slight honor to either the common glory of being a man or the subtleties of learning. Teilhard's effort to convert evolution, a subtle and detailed scientific principle of explanation, into a directed force—what he calls "evolutionary gravity" —makes one shudder over both his confusion and the fact that such reflection gives solace to so many. And the suggestion that one's capabilities in the new life in Christ could in any way be dependent upon the vast and complicated process described by evolutionary theory sets the mind to boggling. In such a scheme even the grossest deviation in a single life is dwarfed into insignificance, vanishes into a nothing. This seems to me a slander upon the Christian story and upon our common humanity. The natural process matters not in the least. What matters is you and I!

Thus the logic of our concepts combines with considerations that are drawn from the life of faith to make us wary of single explanations and all-inclusive accounts. To put it another way: there are indeed several accounts, and each is about everything. We must learn the appropriate manners respecting each. The wisdom of life lies not in some yet undiscovered "what," some new synthesis, but in the "how," in the manner in which we conduct ourselves.

BIBLIOGRAPHY

The following bibliography is not intended to be exhaustive, but it should serve to assist the reader in proceeding more deeply into the issues that this book touches upon. For further readings, the reader is referred to the massive listings in Ian Barbour, *Issues in Science and Religion;* Gail Kennedy, *Evolution and Religion;* and to the periodical, *Zygon,* published by the University of Chicago Press.

1. CONTEMPORARY THEOLOGICAL DISCUSSIONS

Gilkey, Langdon. *Maker of Heaven and Earth.* Garden City: Doubleday & Company, 1959. Paperback.

Haroutunian, Joseph. "Toward a Piety of Faith," in Philip Hefner (ed.), *The Scope of Grace: Essays on Nature and Grace in Honor of Joseph Sittler.* Philadelphia: Fortress Press, 1964.

Heschel, Abraham. *Who Is Man?* Stanford: Stanford University Press, 1965.

Kuemmel, Werner. *Man in the New Testament.* Philadelphia: Westminster, 1963.

Meland, Bernard. "New Perspectives on Nature and Grace," in Philip Hefner (ed.), *The Scope of Grace: Essays on Nature and Grace in Honor of Joseph Sittler.* Philadelphia: Fortress Press, 1964.

Nicholls, William (ed.). *Conflicting Images of Man.* New York: Seabury Press, 1966.

Niebuhr, Reinhold. *The Nature and Destiny of Man.* New York: Scribner's, 1949. Paperback.

Overman, Richard. *Evolution and the Christian Doctrine of Creation.* Philadelphia: Westminster, 1967.

Rahner, Karl. *Hominisation: The Evolutionary Origin of Man as a Theological Problem.* New York: Herder and Herder, 1965. Paperback.

2. The Thought of Teilhard de Chardin

Teilhard de Chardin, Pierre. *The Appearance of Man.* New York: Harper and Row, 1965.

——. *The Future of Man.* New York: Harper and Row, 1964.

——. *The Divine Milieu.* New York: Harper Torchbook, 1965. Paperback.

——. *Man's Place in Nature.* New York: Harper and Row, 1966.

——. *The Phenomenon of Man.* New York: Harper Torchbook, 1961. Paperback.

de Lubac, Henri. *The Faith of Teilhard de Chardin.* London: Burns and Oates, 1965.

Mooney, Christopher. *Teilhard de Chardin and the Mystery of Christ.* New York: Harper and Row, 1966.

3. Contemporary Philosophical Discussions

3a. FREEDOM AND DETERMINISM

Adler, Mortimer. *The Idea of Freedom.* Garden City: Doubleday & Company, 1958, 1961. 2 vols.

Hook, Sidney (ed.). *Determinism and Freedom in the Age of Modern Science.* New York: Collier Books, 1961. Paperback.

Morgenbesser, S. and Danto, A. (ed.). *Free Will.* Englewood Cliffs, New Jersey: Prentice-Hall, 1965. Paperback.

3b. METAPHYSICS

Alexander, S. C. *Space, Time, and Deity.* New York: Dover Books, 1965. 2 vols. Paperback.

Hartshorne, Charles. *Reality as Social Process.* Glencoe, Illinois: The Free Press, 1953.

Whitehead, Alfred N. *Process and Reality.* New York: Harper Torchbook. Paperback.

3c. CHANGE

Van Melsen, Andreas. *Evolution and Philosophy*. Pittsburgh: Duquesne University Press, 1965.

3d. PHILOSOPHY OF SCIENCE

Frank, Philipp. *Philosophy of Science*. Englewood Cliffs, New Jersey: Prentice-Hall, 1957. Paperback.

Jonas, Hans. *The Phenomenon of Life: Toward a Philosophical Biology*. New York: Harper and Row, 1966.

Kuhn, Thomas. *The Structure of Scientific Revolutions*. Chicago: University of Chicago Press, 1962. Paperback.

Margenau, Henry. *Open Vistas*. New Haven: Yale University Press, 1961. Paperback.

Nagel, Ernest. *The Structure of Science*. New York: Harcourt, Brace, and World, 1961.

4. PERTINENT WORKS OF CONTEMPORARY SCIENTISTS

Alland, Alexander. *Evolution and Human Behavior*. Garden City: Natural History Press, 1967.

Anderson, A. R. (ed.). *Minds and Machines*. Englewood Cliffs, New Jersey: Prentice-Hall, 1964. Paperback.

Dobzhansky, Theodosius. *The Biological Basis of Human Freedom*. New York: Columbia University Press, 1960. Paperback.

——. *The Biology of Ultimate Concern*. New York: New American Library, 1967.

——. *Heredity and the Nature of Man*. New York: Harcourt, Brace, and World, 1964.

——. *Mankind Evolving*. New Haven: Yale University Press, 1962. Paperback.

Dubos, René. *Man Adapting*. New Haven: Yale University Press, 1965.

Huxley, Julian. *Evolution in Action*. New York: Harper and Row, 1953. Paperback.

——. *Religion Without Revelation*. New York: New American Library, 1957. Paperback.

Keeton, William. *Biological Science*. New York: W. W. Norton and Co., 1967.

La Barre, Weston. *The Human Animal*. Chicago: University of Chicago Press, 1954. Paperback.

Lwoff, André. *Biological Order*. Cambridge, Massachusetts: M.I.T. Press, 1965. Paperback.

Tax, Sol (ed.). *Evolution After Darwin*. Chicago: University of Chicago Press, 1960. 3 vols.

5. RELEVANT WORKS IN THE SOCIAL SCIENCES

Berger, Peter. *Invitation to Sociology: A Humanistic Perspective*. New York: Doubleday Anchor Books, 1963. Paperback.

Glock, Charles, and Stark, Rodney. *Religion and Society in Tension*. Chicago: Rand McNally and Co., 1965. See chaps. 14 and 15.

Goffman, Erving. *The Presentation of Self in Everyday Life*. New York: Doubleday Anchor Books, 1959. Paperback.

Mills, C. Wright (ed.). *Images of Man: The Classic Tradition in Sociological Thinking*. New York: Braziller, 1960.

6. HISTORICAL WORKS

Benz, Ernst. *Evolution and Christian Hope: Man's Concept of the Future from the Early Fathers to Teilhard de Chardin*. Garden City: Doubleday & Company, 1966. Paperback.

Dillenberger, John. *Protestant Thought and Natural Science*. Garden City: Doubleday & Company, 1960.

Eiseley, Loren. *Darwin's Century*. Garden City: Doubleday Anchor Books, 1961. Paperback.

Greene, John. *Darwin and the Modern World View*. New York: New American Library, 1963. Paperback.

——. *The Death of Adam*. New York: New American Library, 1959. Paperback.

Kennedy, Gail (ed.). *Evolution and Religion: The Conflict*

between Science and Theology in Modern America. Boston: D. C. Heath and Co., 1957. Paperback.

Whitehead, Alfred N. *Science and the Modern World.* New York: Macmillan, 1926. Paperback.

7. WORKS PERTINENT TO THE DIALOGUE BETWEEN BIOLOGY AND CHRISTIAN FAITH

Barbour, Ian. *Issues in Science and Religion.* Englewood Cliffs, New Jersey: Prentice-Hall, 1966.

Fothergill, P. G. *Evolution and Christians.* London: Longman's, Green and Co., Ltd., 1961.

Heim, Karl. *Christian Faith and Natural Science.* New York: Harper Torchbooks, 1953. Paperback.

Hook, Sidney (ed.). *Dimensions of Mind.* New York: Collier Books, 1960. Paperback.

Messenger, E. C. *Theology and Evolution.* Westminster, Maryland: Newman, 1952.

Ong, Walter (ed.). *Darwin's Vision and Christian Perspectives.* New York: Macmillan, 1960.

Shideler, Emerson. *Believing and Knowing.* Ames, Iowa: Iowa State University Press, 1966.

von Weizsacker, C. F. *The Relevance of Science: Creation and Cosmogeny.* London: Collins, 1964.

8. WORKS RELEVANT TO THE ETHICS OF BIO-TECHNOLOGY

Dubos, René. *The Torch of Life.* New York: Simon and Schuster, 1962.

Fletcher, Joseph. *Morals and Medicine.* Princeton: Princeton University Press, 1954.

Glass, Bentley. *Science and Ethical Values.* Chapel Hill: University of North Carolina Press, 1965.

Holton, Gerald (ed.). *Science and Culture.* Boston: Houghton Mifflin Co., 1965.

INDEX

ANCHOR BOOKS

Religion (continued)

ANCHOR BOOKS

SOCIOLOGY

Sociology (continued)

Sociology (continued)

ANCHOR BOOKS

ANTHROPOLOGY AND ARCHAEOLOGY

ANCHOR BOOKS

NATURAL HISTORY LIBRARY